GRADED GO PROBLEMS
FOR BEGINNERS

VOLUME THREE
INTERMEDIATE PROBLEMS

by

Kano Yoshinori 9-dan

The Nihon Ki-in

Published by
The Nihon Ki-in
7-2 Gobancho,
Chiyoda-ku, Tokyo,
Japan

Distributed by The Ishi Press, Inc.
CPO Box 2126, Tokyo, Japan

In North America, order from:
THE ISHI PRESS INTERNATIONAL, INC.
1101 San Antonio Road, Suite 302
Mountain View, Calif. 94043

In Europe, order from:
Dietmar Hartung
Bundesalle 126
1000 Berlin 41
West Germany

First Printing March 1987
Printed in Japan
by
Sokosha Printing Co., Ltd.
Typeset on an IBM Electronic Composer
by The Ishi Press, Inc.

TABLE OF CONTENTS

PREFACE

This volume is a continuation of the second volume of GRADED GO PROBLEMS FOR BEGINNERS and is aimed at the 15-kyu to 20-kyu player.

The problems presented here will require some thought, but none of them is so difficult that a player who understands the rules, has had some experience playing games, and has studied the first and second volumes of this series would not be able to solve them in less than a minute.

Since the aim of this series is to present as many examples of go technique as possible, I have avoided giving a lot of different variations of possible answers. The reader is advised to attempt to 'refute' the correct answer until he knows beyond a doubt that the correct answer does in fact work. By pondering cach problem in this way, the reader will develop an instinct for finding the winning move in his games.

March, 1987   Kano Yoshinori 9-dan

GLOSSARY

atari — check, i.e. a move threatening to capture on the next move.

dame — neutral points which profit neither Black nor White.

dan — a rank given to players to indicate their strength at the game. When a player's strength improves after attaining the rank of 1-kyu, he is promoted to amateur 1-dan and as he becomes stronger, the numerical value of his *dan* increases. The top amateur dan rank is usually 6-dan. The professional dan ranks start at 1-dan and go up to 9-dan, which is the highest rank attainable. A professional 1-dan is usually about two stones stronger than an amateur 6-dan. See *kyu*.

double atari — giving atari to two different groups of stones at the same time.

eye — a point on the board which is surrounded by stones of the same color.

ko — a shape in which your stone is captured but it is illegal to retake the capturing stones even though you can occupy all of its liberties.

kyu — a rank given to players to indicate their strength at the game. Beginners are arbitrarily classified at 30-kyu and as they become stronger, the numerical value of their *kyu* decreases. For example, 15-kyu is stronger than 20-kyu. See *dan*.

nakade — a large eye-space which, by skillful play, can be reduced to a single eye.

oiotoshi — a move which gives atari to a group of stones in such a way that no matter how one defends, the group will still be in atari.

oshitsubushi — a shape in which you give atari to two or more of your opponent's stones in such a way that he cannot defend against this atari without committing suicide.

seki — an impasse or stalemate between groups: if one side tries to attack the other side's group, his own group is put into atari and dies. Therefore, neither side can attack or attempt to atari.

snapback — a tactic in which one stone is offered as a sacrifice and if it is taken, the capturing stones are in turn captured.

PART ONE

PROBLEMS

I INTERMEDIATE PROBLEMS
LEVEL ONE

SECTION 1. MIDDLE-GAME PROBLEMS

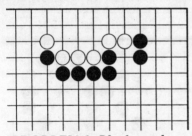

PROBLEM 1. Black to play.
How should Black play so as to completely surround the white stones?

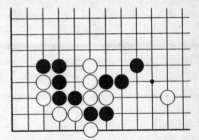

PROBLEM 2. Black to play.
Black should play so as to prevent the capture of his two stones on the second line.

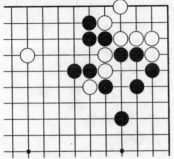

PROBLEM 3. White to play.
How can White play so as to escape with his two stones in the centre?

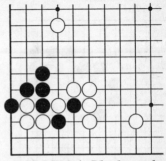

PROBLEM 4. Black to play.
What is Black's best move?

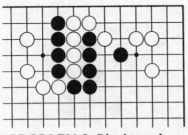

PROBLEM 5. Black to play.
How should Black play?

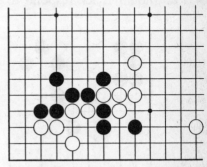

PROBLEM 6. Black to play.
The first thing Black should do is make sure that his two stones at the bottom cannot be captured.

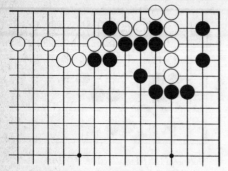

PROBLEM 7. Black to play.
How should Black play so as to capture the eight white stones on the right?

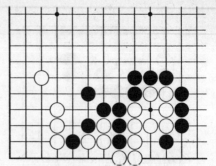

PROBLEM 8. Black to play.
How should Black play so as to capture the thirteen white stones on the right?

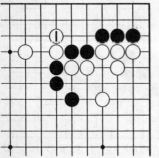

PROBLEM 9. Black to play.
How should Black respond to White 1?

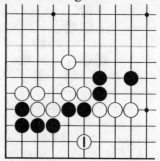

PROBLEM 10. Black to play.
How should Black respond to White 1?

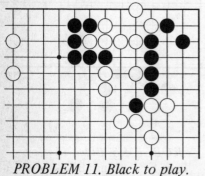

PROBLEM 11. Black to play.
How should Black play so as to capture the seven white stones at the top?

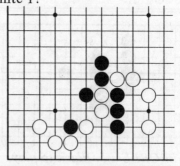

PROBLEM 12. Black to play.
How should Black play so as to capture the two white stones in the center?

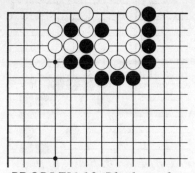

PROBLEM 13. Black to play.
How should Black play so as to capture seven white stones?

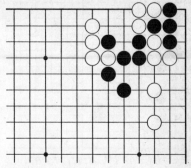

PROBLEM 14. White to play.
How should White play so as to link up his three stones at the top to the ones on the left?

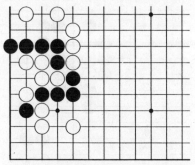

PROBLEM 15. White to play.
How can White save his five endangered stones?

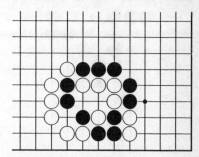

PROBLEM 16. White to play.
How can White capture six black stones?

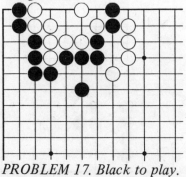

PROBLEM 17. Black to play.
Black has a move which will create a ko for the life of the white stones on the left.

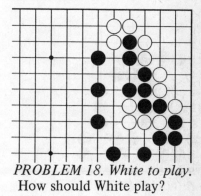

PROBLEM 18. White to play.
How should White play?

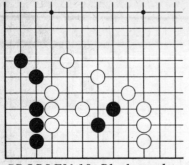

PROBLEM 19. Black to play.
How can Black link up his stones on the right to the ones on the left?

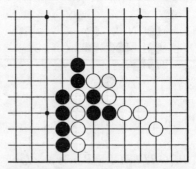

PROBLEM 20. Black to play.
How can Black capture eight white stones?

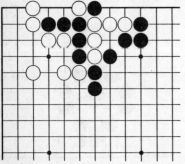

PROBLEM 21. Black to play.
How can Black win the capturing race?

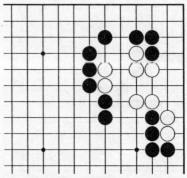

PROBLEM 22. Black to play.
If you strike at the vital point, you can kill the white stones.

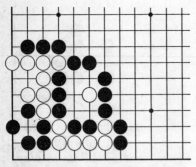

PROBLEM 23. White to play.
What is White's best move?

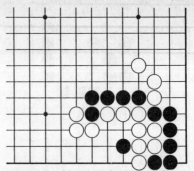

PROBLEM 24. Black to play.
How can Black capture four white stones?

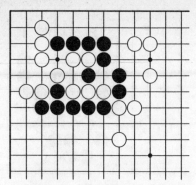

PROBLEM 25. Black to play.
How can Black capture some of White's stones?

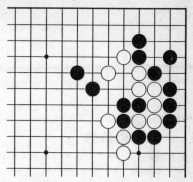

PROBLEM 26. White to play.
How can White capture three black stones?

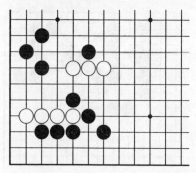

PROBLEM 27. White to play.
How can White link up his two groups?

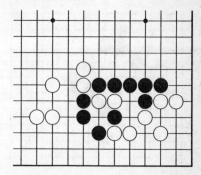

PROBLEM 28. White to play.
How should White play?

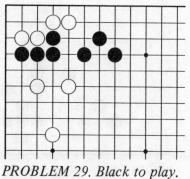

PROBLEM 29. Black to play.
How does Black kill the white stones in the corner?

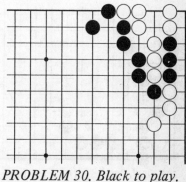

PROBLEM 30. Black to play.
How can Black capture the white stones in the corner?

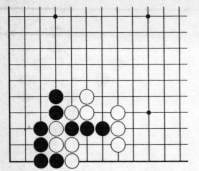

PROBLEM 31. White to play.
How can White capture three black stones?

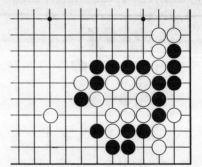

PROBLEM 32. White to play.
How should White play?

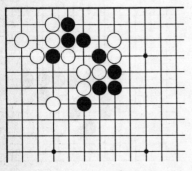

PROBLEM 33. Black to play.
How should Black play?

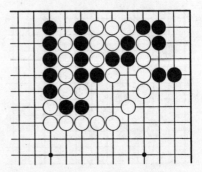

PROBLEM 34. Black to play.
Here you are asked to capture either five or six white stones.

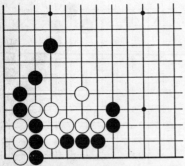

PROBLEM 35. Black to play.
How should Black play?

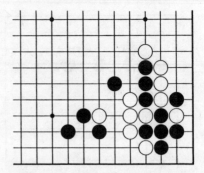

PROBLEM 36. White to play.
How can White capture three black stones?

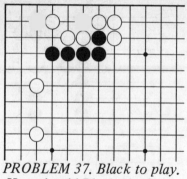

PROBLEM 37. *Black to play.*
How should Black play?

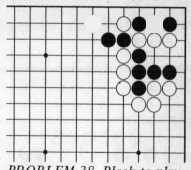

PROBLEM 38. *Black to play.*
How can Black capture three white stones?

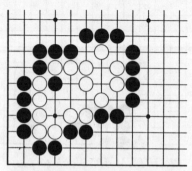

PROBLEM 39. *Black to play.*
How should Black play so as to capture all the white stones?

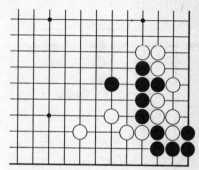

PROBLEM 40. *Black to play.*
How should Black play so as to capture four white stones?

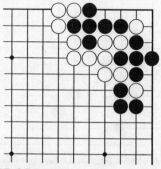

PROBLEM 41. *Black to play.*
How should Black play so as to secure all his stones?

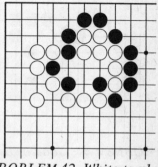

PROBLEM 42. *White to play.*
How can White save his seven endangered stones?

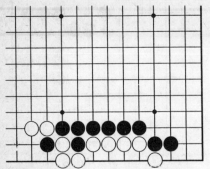

PROBLEM 43. Black to play.
How should Black play so as to capture the eight white stones on the edge?

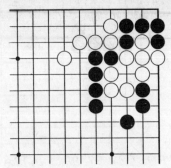

PROBLEM 44. Black to play.
How should Black play?

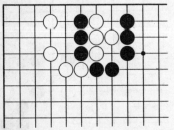

PROBLEM 45. White to play.
How should White play so as to capture three black stones?

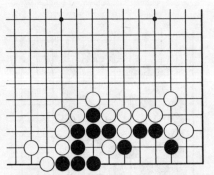

PROBLEM 46. Black to play.
How should Black play?

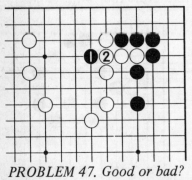

PROBLEM 47. Good or bad?
Is peeping at 1, forcing White to connect at 2, a good or a bad move?

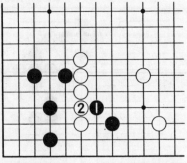

PROBLEM 48. Good or bad?
Is peeping at 1, forcing White to connect at 2, a good or a bad move?

PROBLEM 49
Black to play.

Among the points A through D, which is the most important one for Black to play?

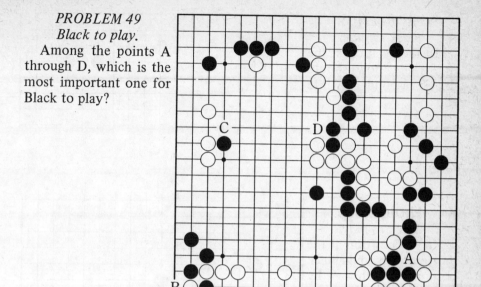

SECTION 2. OPENING PROBLEMS

PROBLEM 50
Black to play.

In the position at the top right, how should Black respond to White 1?

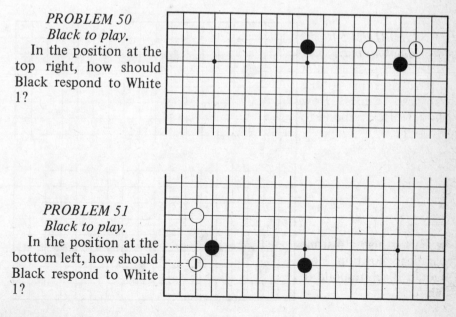

PROBLEM 51
Black to play.

In the position at the bottom left, how should Black respond to White 1?

PROBLEM 52
Black to play.
In the position at the top right, how should Black respond to White 1?

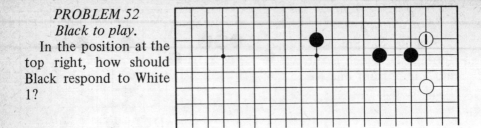

PROBLEM 53
Black to play.
In the position at the bottom left, should Black respond to White 1 by attaching at A or B?

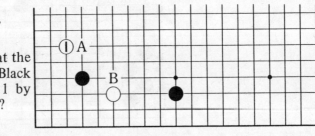

PROBLEM 54
Black to play.
This is a position that often arises in 4-stone handicap games. How should Black respond to White 1?

PROBLEM 55
Black to play.
This is also a 4-stone handicap position. How should Black respond to White 1?

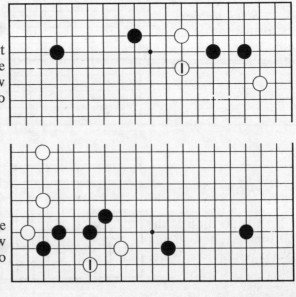

PROBLEM 56
Black to play.

In the opening, it is sometimes more important to play on an urgent point than to map out territory. In this position, where should Black play?

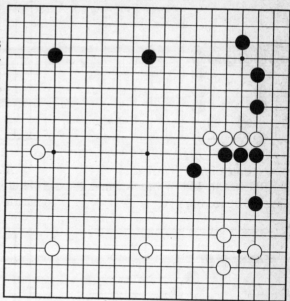

SECTION 3. LIVING GROUPS AND DEAD GROUPS

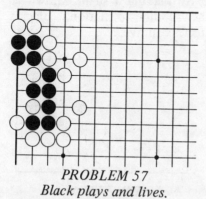

PROBLEM 57
Black plays and lives.

If you know the under-the-stones tactic, you will have no trouble solving this problem.

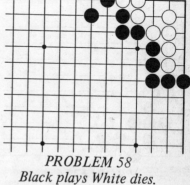

PROBLEM 58
Black plays White dies.

You can kill White by making a bent-four-in-the-corner shape.

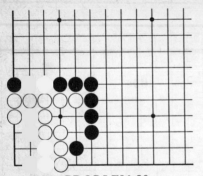

PROBLEM 59
Black plays White dies.
Black can kill White by making a 6-space big eye.

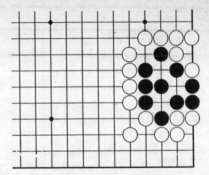

PROBLEM 60
Black plays and lives.
There is a double ko in this position. How does Black live?

PROBLEM 61
Black plays White dies.
Black's first move decides the fate of the white group.

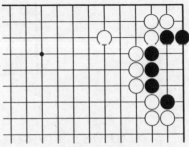

PROBLEM 62
Black plays and lives.
By making a shape known as the 'comb formation', Black's stones can live.

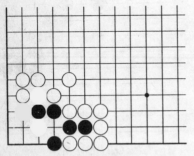

PROBLEM 63
Black plays and lives.
Black has to sacrifice two stones if he is going to live.

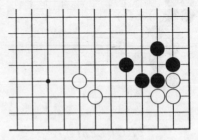

PROBLEM 64
Black plays White dies.
Kill the three white stones in the corner.

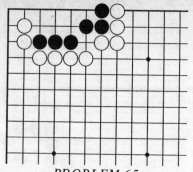

PROBLEM 65
Black plays and lives.
Make two eyes for the black group.

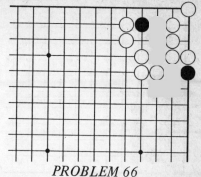

PROBLEM 66
Black plays and makes a ko.
If you sacrifice a stone two times, you can get a ko.

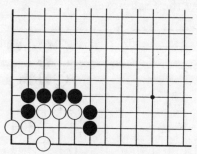

PROBLEM 67
Black plays White dies.
Since three of White's stones are short of liberties, the whole white group dies.

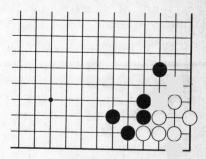

PROBLEM 68
Black plays and makes a ko.
Black can kill White by making a ko.

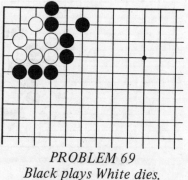

PROBLEM 69
Black plays White dies.
If you use the stone on the 1st line, you can kill White.

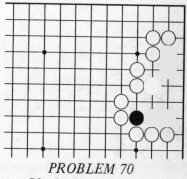

PROBLEM 70
Black plays and lives.
You have to play on the vital point.

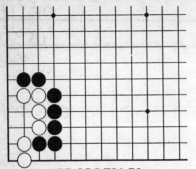

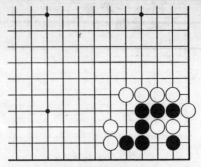

PROBLEM 71
Black plays White dies.

Since four of White's stones are short of liberties, all the white stones die.

PROBLEM 72
Black plays and lives.

Be a bit cautious before playing the first move.

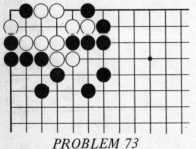

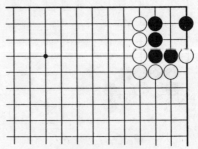

PROBLEM 73
Black plays White dies.

You can kill White by taking advantage of his shortage of liberties.

PROBLEM 74
Black plays and lives.

Black has to play on the vital point.

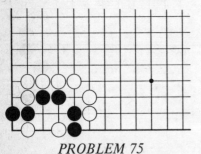

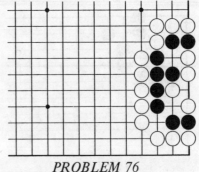

PROBLEM 75
Black plays and lives.

Black can live by making a seki.

PROBLEM 76
Black plays and lives.

Black can live by sacrificing two stones.

SECTION 4. ENDGAME PROBLEMS

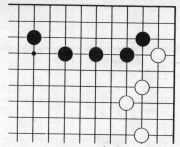

PROBLEM 77. Black to play.
Make a big endgame move.

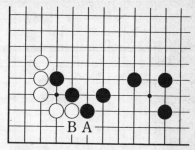

PROBLEM 78. White to play.
In general, which is the bigger endgame move, A or B?

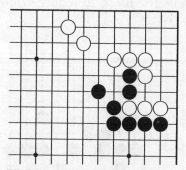

PROBLEM 79. Black to play.
How should Black play the endgame on the right?

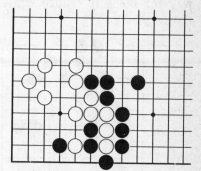

PROBLEM 80. White to play.
What is White's most profitable move?

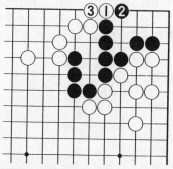

PROBLEM 81. Black to play.
How should Black play after White 1 and 3?

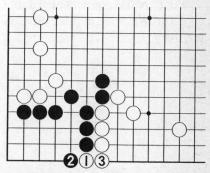

PROBLEM 82. Black to play.
What is the most profitable way for Black to respond to White 1 and 3?

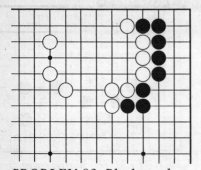

PROBLEM 83. Black to play.
What is the most profitable way for Black to reduce White's territory?

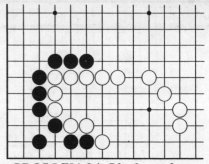

PROBLEM 84. Black to play.
What is the most profitable way for Black to reduce White's territory?

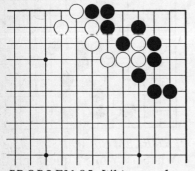

PROBLEM 85. White to play.
What is the most profitable way for White to reduce Black's territory?

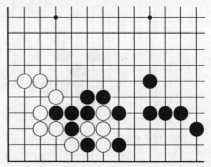

PROBLEM 86. Black to play.
What is the most profitable way for Black to atari the four white stones?

II INTERMEDIATE PROBLEMS
LEVEL TWO

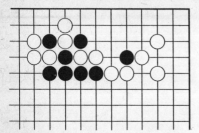

PROBLEM 87. Black to play.
How should Black play in order to capture two white stones?

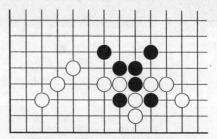

PROBLEM 88. Black to play.
How should Black play in order to capture two white stones?

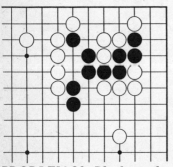

PROBLEM 89. Black to play.
How does Black take advantage of White's shortage of liberties?

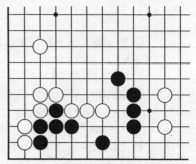

PROBLEM 90. White to play.
In order to separate Black into two groups, White has to sacrifice a stone.

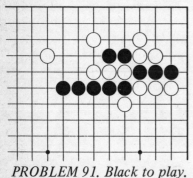

PROBLEM 91. Black to play.
By sacrificing the three stones on the right using a squeeze tactic, Black can get a good position.

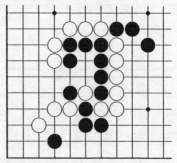

PROBLEM 92. White to play.
How should White sacrifice his stone in atari?

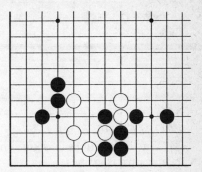

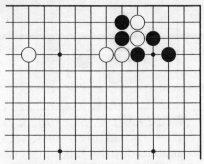

PROBLEM 93. *White to play.*
White is going to sacrifice two stones. What is the correct order of moves?

PROBLEM 94. *White to play.*
Should White sacrifice or save his stone in atari?

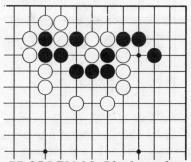

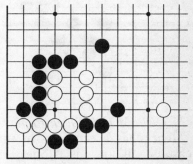

PROBLEM 95. *Black to play.*
How should Black play in order to capture three white stones?

PROBLEM 96. *Black to play.*
Black can capture the five white stones in the corner.

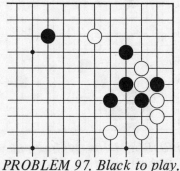

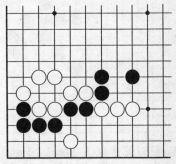

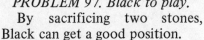

PROBLEM 97. *Black to play.*
By sacrificing two stones, Black can get a good position.

PROBLEM 98. *Black to play.*
Black can capture one stone. How should he play?

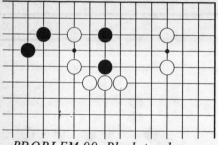

PROBLEM 99. Black to play.

If Black sacrifices a stone, he can link up his stones.

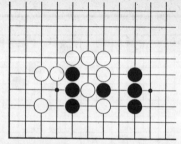

PROBLEM 100. Black to play.

How should Black play so as to unconditionally link up his two groups?

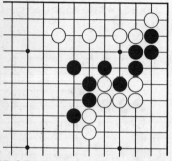

PROBLEM 101. Black to play.

Black has a sente move that ensures all of his stones are connected.

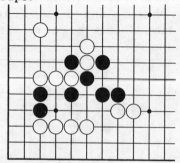

PROBLEM 102. Black to play.

Black has a sente move that ensures all of his stones are connected.

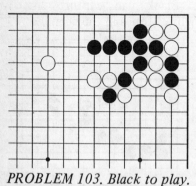

PROBLEM 103. Black to play.

All the black stones are in danger. How can some of them be saved?

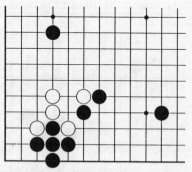

PROBLEM 104. White to play.

Black's position is thin. How should White play?

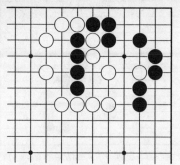

PROBLEM 105. Black to play.
How should Black play so as to rescue his four endangered stones?

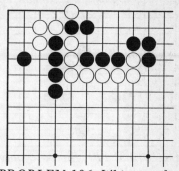

PROBLEM 106. White to play.
How can White capture two black stones and rescue his four stones in the corner?

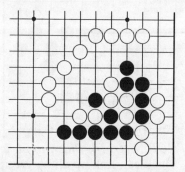

PROBLEM 107. Black to play.
How can Black capture four white stones?

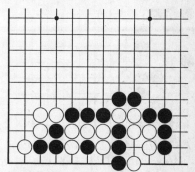

PROBLEM 108. Black to play.
How does Black play so as to capture six white stones?

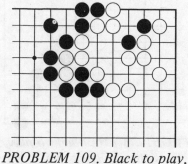

PROBLEM 109. Black to play.
Where should Black cut?

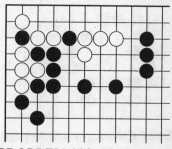

PROBLEM 110. Black to play.
By sacrificing a stone, Black can separate White into two groups.

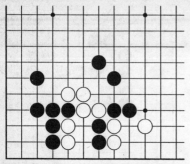

PROBLEM 111. *Black to play.*
Save Black's two endangered stones.

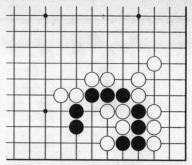

PROBLEM 112. *Black to play.*
How does Black play so as to capture three white stones?

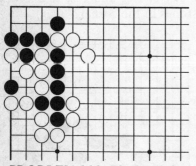

PROBLEM 113. *Black to play.*
How can Black capture five white stones?

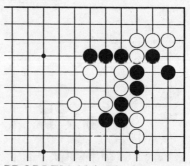

PROBLEM 114. *Black to play.*
Black can link up all his groups by capturing two white stones.

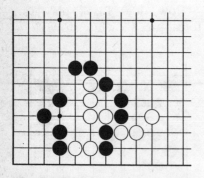

PROBLEM 115. *Black to play.*
How can Black save his two endangered stones and capture six white ones?

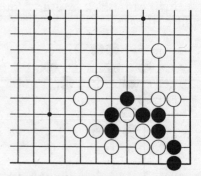

PROBLEM 116. *Black to play.*
How should Black play?

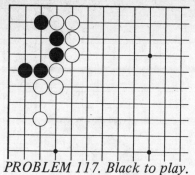

PROBLEM 117. Black to play.
If Black plays the 'shape' move, his five stones will live.

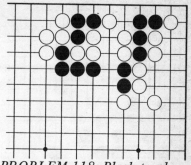

PROBLEM 118. Black to play.
How can Black capture two white stones?

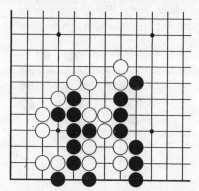

PROBLEM 119. White to play.
How does White prevent the black groups from linking up?

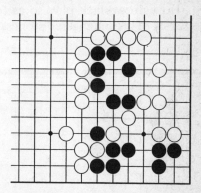

PROBLEM 120. Black to play.
Black can link up his two groups by sacrificing a stone.

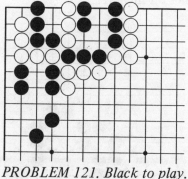

PROBLEM 121. Black to play.
Black can break the seki and capture eight white stones.

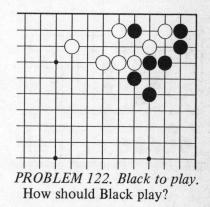

PROBLEM 122. Black to play.
How should Black play?

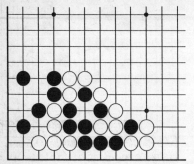

PROBLEM 123. Black to play.
How does Black play so as to save six of his endangered stones?

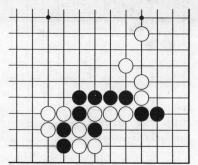

PROBLEM 124. Black to play.
How does Black play so as to capture three white stones?

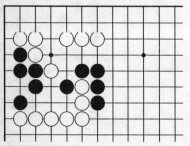

PROBLEM 125. Black to play.
Black has to sacrifice a stone in order to connect his groups.

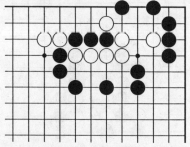

PROBLEM 126. Black to play.
How does Black link up his three endangered stones to the ones on the left?

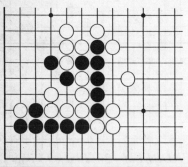

PROBLEM 127. Black to play.
Capture six white stones.

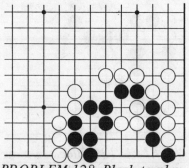

PROBLEM 128. Black to play.
Capture three white stones.

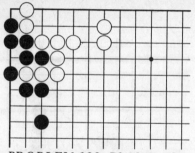

PROBLEM 129. Black to play.
How can Black prevent five of his stones from being captured and get sente at the same time?

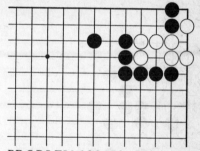

PROBLEM 130. Black to play.
Link up Black's two stones in the corner to the ones on the left.

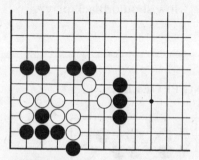

PROBLEM 131. Black to play.
Link up Black's five stones in the corner to the ones on the right.

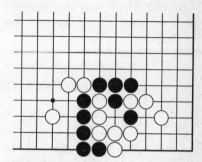

PROBLEM 132. Black to play.
How should Black play so as to capture six white stones?

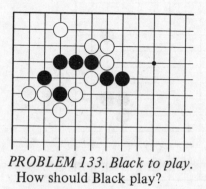

PROBLEM 133. Black to play.
How should Black play?

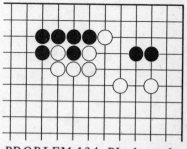

PROBLEM 134. Black to play.
Link up the two black stones in the corner to the ones on the left.

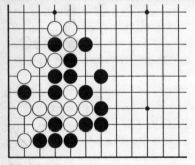

PROBLEM 135. Black to play.
Before Black can capture any white stones, he must correct the defect in his shape.

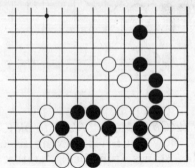

PROBLEM 136. Black to play.
How should Black play?

SECTION 2. OPENING PROBLEMS

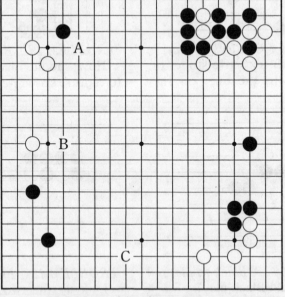

PROBLEM 137. White to play.
Among the three points A, B and C, which one is the best?

— 28 —

PROBLEM 138
Black to play.
Among the three points A, B and C, which one is best?

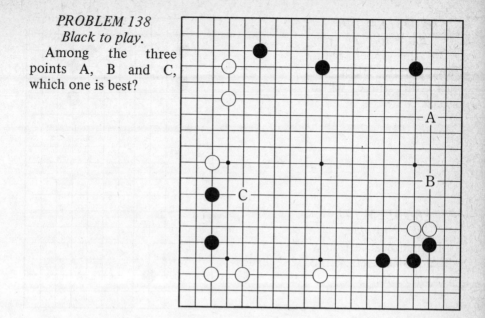

PROBLEM 139
Black to play.
Black has two good ways of responding to White 1. What are they?

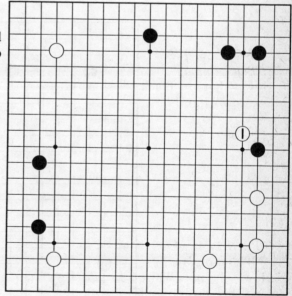

PROBLEM 140
Black to play.
In the upper right, how should Black attack the three white stones?

PROBLEM 141
Black to play.
In the lower left, how should Black attack the white position?

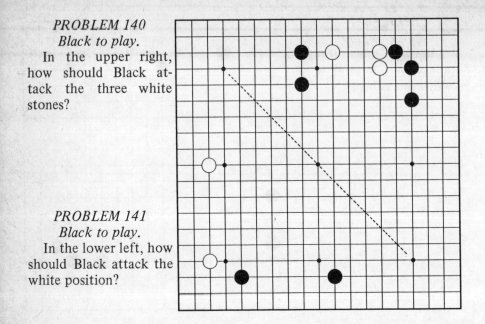

PROBLEM 142
Black to play.
How should Black respond to White 1?

PROBLEM 143
White to play.
How should White defend his position at the bottom?

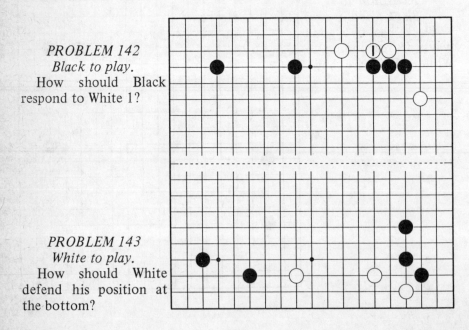

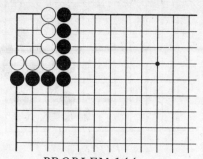

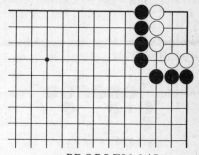

PROBLEM 144
Black plays White dies.
Black can unconditionally kill White.

PROBLEM 145
Black plays and makes a ko.
The only way to kill White is through a ko.

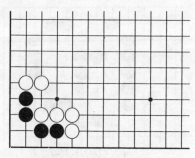

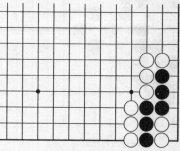

PROBLEM 146
Black plays and lives.
You have to play on the 1—2 point, but which one?

PROBLEM 147
Black plays and lives.
There is a clever move which relieves Black's shortage of liberties and gives him two eyes.

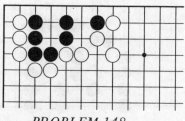

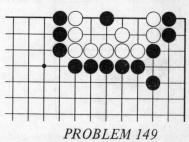

PROBLEM 148
Black plays and lives.
Black needs space to make two eyes.

PROBLEM 149
Black plays White dies.
If Black sacrifices a stone, White dies.

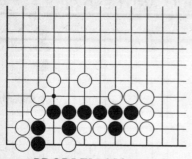

PROBLEM 150
Black plays and lives.

Black can live by sacrificing a stone.

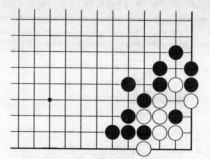

PROBLEM 151
Black plays White dies.

Black has to make a two-stone sacrifice in order to kill White.

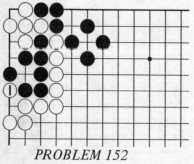

PROBLEM 152
Black plays and wins.

Black can capture the five white stones in the corner by starting a double ko.

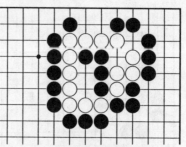

PROBLEM 153
Black plays White dies.

You can kill White by making a 5-space big eye.

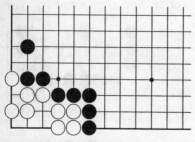

PROBLEM 154
Black plays White dies.

Your first inspiration may not be the correct move.

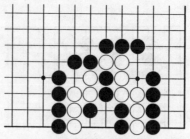

PROELEM 155
Black plays White dies.

You can kill White by making a 6-space big eye.

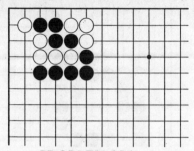

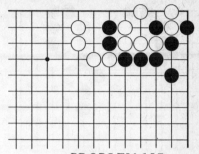

PROBLEM 156
Black plays and makes a ko.
Black can consider it a success
if he can get a ko in the corner.

PROBLEM 157
Black plays and wins.
Black can capture the seven
white stones in the corner.

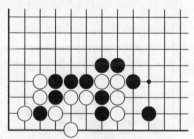

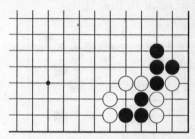

PROBLEM 158
Black plays and wins.
How can Black play so as to
capture four white stones?

PROBLEM 159
Black plays and wins.
Black can win the capturing
race by striking at the vital point
in the corner.

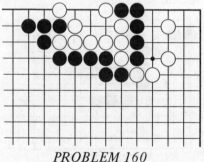

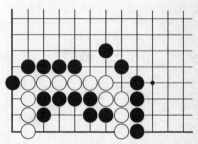

PROBLEM 160
White plays and wins.
First of all, White has to increase his liberties. Then he can
win the capturing race.

PROBLEM 161
Black plays and wins.
A 5-space big eye gives you
eight liberties. With this hint,
kill White.

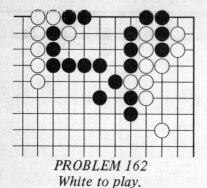

PROBLEM 162
White to play.

There is a move that will catch either two black stones on the left or four on the right.

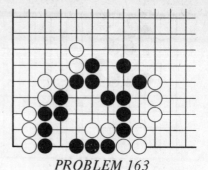

PROBLEM 163
White to play

If you take advantage of Black's shortage of liberties, you can capture three of his stones.

PROBLEM 164
Black to play

With a little thought you can capture a white stone without getting involved in a ko fight.

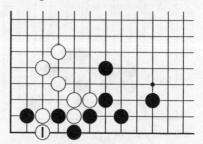

PROBLEM 165
Black to play.

White 1 is a bad move. How should Black play?

PROBLEM 166
White to play.

If you know the 'monkey jump', you can make a big reduction in Black's territory.

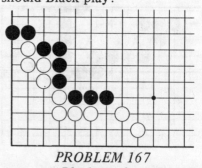

PROBLEM 167
Black to play.

White's four stones on the left are short of liberties. How does Black take advantage of this?

PROBLEM 168. Black to play.

In the position at the top, what is the most profitable way for Black to invade White's territory?

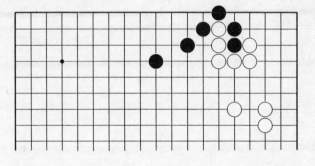

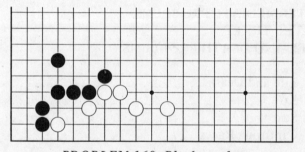

PROBLEM 169. Black to play.

In the position at the bottom, what is the most profitable move for Black?

III INTERMEDIATE PROBLEMS
     LEVEL THREE
     LIFE AND DEATH PROBLEMS

SECTION 1. LIFE AND DEATH

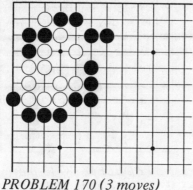

PROBLEM 170 (3 moves)
Black plays White dies.

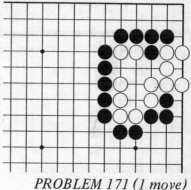

PROBLEM 171 (1 move)
Black plays White dies.

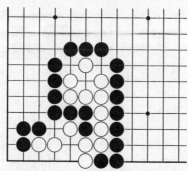

PROBLEM 172 (3 moves)
Black plays White dies.

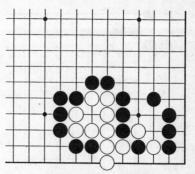

PROBLEM 173 (3 moves)
Black plays White dies.

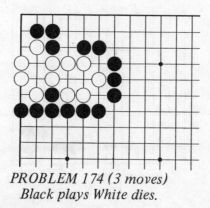

PROBLEM 174 (3 moves)
Black plays White dies.

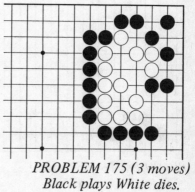

PROBLEM 175 (3 moves)
Black plays White dies.

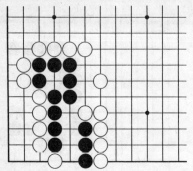

PROBLEM 176 (3 moves)
Black plays and lives.

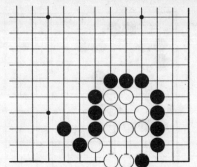

PROBLEM 177 (3 moves)
Black plays White dies.

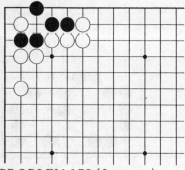

PROBLEM 178 (3 moves)
Black plays and lives.

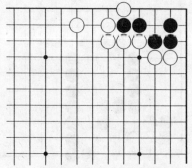

PROBLEM 179 (1 move)
Black plays and lives.

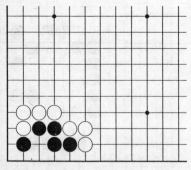

PROBLEM 180 (3 moves)
Black plays and lives.

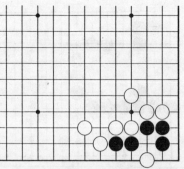

PROBLEM 181 (3 moves)
Black plays and lives.

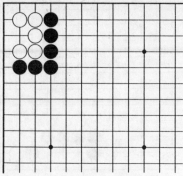

PROBLEM 182 (3 moves)
Black plays White dies.

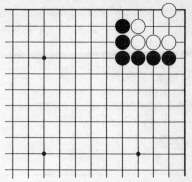

PROBLEM 183 (3 moves)
Black plays White dies.

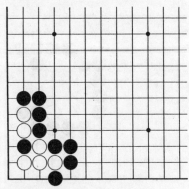

PROBLEM 184 (3 moves)
Black plays White dies.

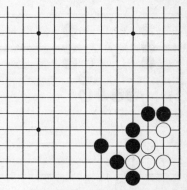

PROBLEM 185 (3 moves)
Black plays White dies.

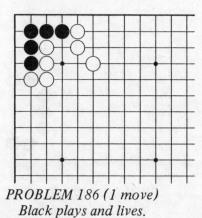

PROBLEM 186 (1 move)
Black plays and lives.

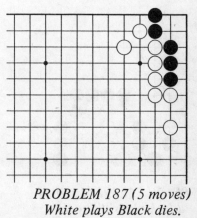

PROBLEM 187 (5 moves)
White plays Black dies.

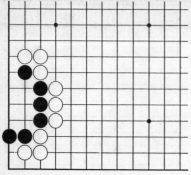

PROBLEM 188 (3 moves)
Black plays and lives.

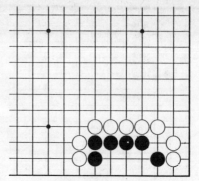

PROBLEM 189 (7 moves)
Black plays and lives.

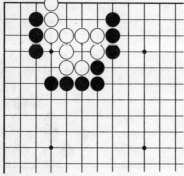

PROBLEM 190 (3 moves)
Black plays White dies.

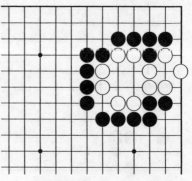

PROBLEM 191 (1 move)
Black plays White dies.

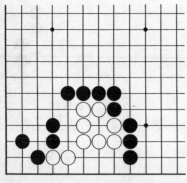

PROBLEM 192 (1 move)
Black plays White dies.

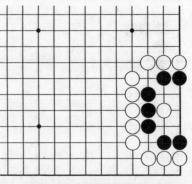

PROBLEM 193 (1 move)
Black plays and lives.

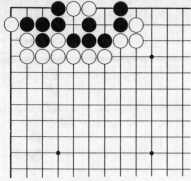

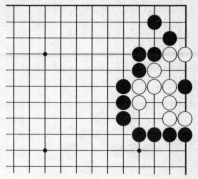

PROBLEM 194 (3 moves)
White plays Black dies.

PROBLEM 195 (3 moves)
Black plays White dies.

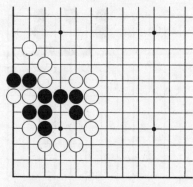

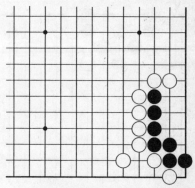

PROBLEM 196 (3 moves)
White plays Black dies.

PROBLEM 197 (1 move)
Black plays and lives.

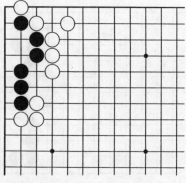

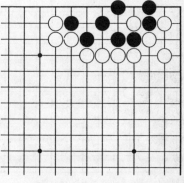

PROBLEM 198 (1 move)
Black plays and lives.

PROBLEM 199 (1 move)
Black plays and lives.

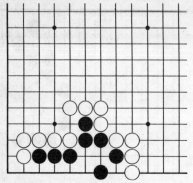

PROBLEM 200 (1 move)
Black plays and lives.

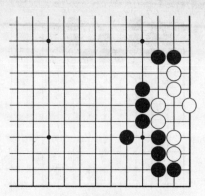

PROBLEM 201 (3 moves)
Black plays White dies.

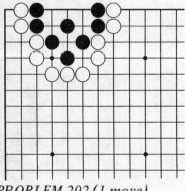

PROBLEM 202 (1 move)
White plays Black dies.

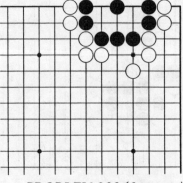

PROBLEM 203 (3 moves)
White plays Black dies.

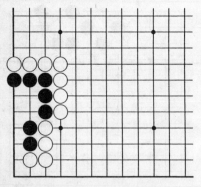

PROBLEM 204 (1 move)
Black plays and lives.

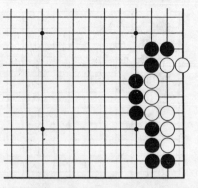

PROBLEM 205 (1 move)
Black plays White dies.

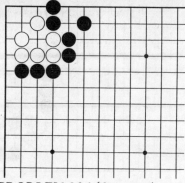

PROBLEM 206 (3 moves)
Black plays White dies.

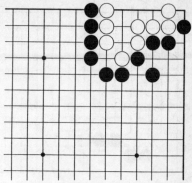

PROBLEM 207 (3 moves)
Black plays White dies.

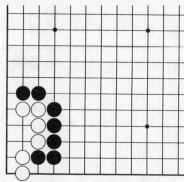

PROBLEM 208 (3 moves)
Black plays White dies.

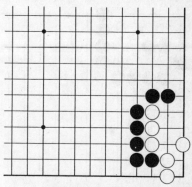

PROBLEM 209 (3 moves)
Black plays White dies.

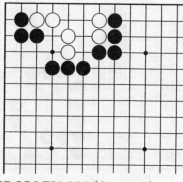

PROBLEM 210 (3 moves)
White plays and lives.

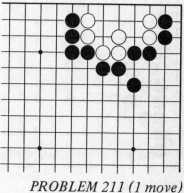

PROBLEM 211 (1 move)
White plays and lives.

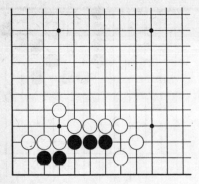

PROBLEM 212 (1 move)
Black plays and lives.

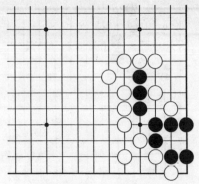

PROBLEM 213 (3 moves)
Black plays and lives.

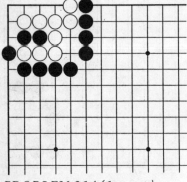

PROBLEM 214 (1 move)
Black plays White dies.

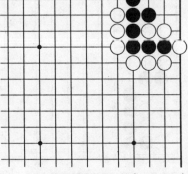

PROBLEM 215 (1 move)
Black plays and lives.

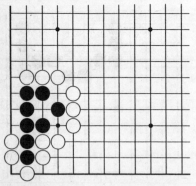

PROBLEM 216 (1 move)
Black plays and lives.

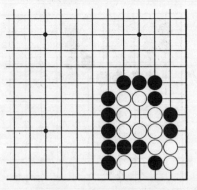

PROBLEM 217 (3 moves)
Black plays White dies.

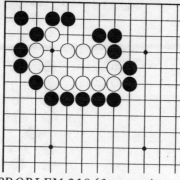

PROBLEM 218 (3 moves)
Black plays White dies.

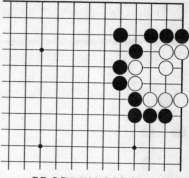

PROBLEM 219 (5 moves)
Black plays White dies.

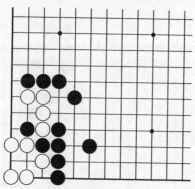

PROBLEM 220 (1 move)
White plays and lives.

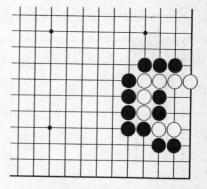

PROBLEM 221 (3 moves)
White plays and lives.

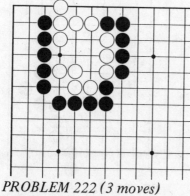

PROBLEM 222 (3 moves)
Black plays White dies.

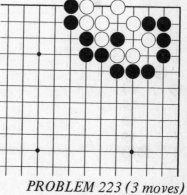

PROBLEM 223 (3 moves)
Black plays White dies.

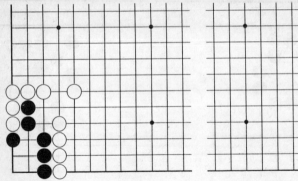

PROBLEM 224 (3 moves)
Black plays and lives.

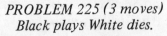

PROBLEM 225 (3 moves)
Black plays White dies.

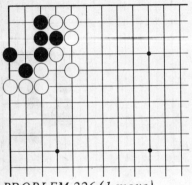

PROBLEM 226 (1 move)
Black plays and lives.

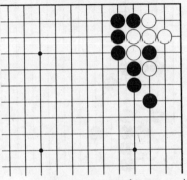

PROBLEM 227 (3 moves)
Black plays White dies.

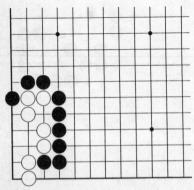

PROBLEM 228 (3 moves)
Black plays White dies.

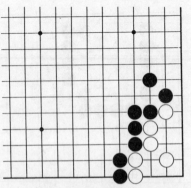

PROBLEM 229 (3 moves)
Black plays White dies.

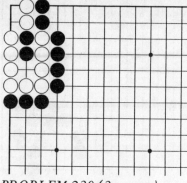

PROBLEM 230 (3 moves)
Black plays White dies.

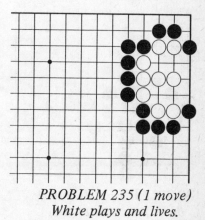

PROBLEM 231 (3 moves)
White plays and lives.

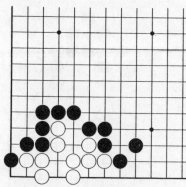

PROBLEM 232 (3 moves)
Black plays White dies.

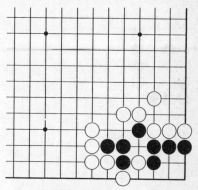

PROBLEM 233 (5 moves)
Black plays and lives.

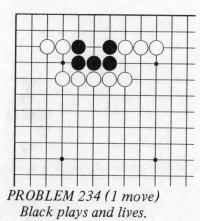

PROBLEM 234 (1 move)
Black plays and lives.

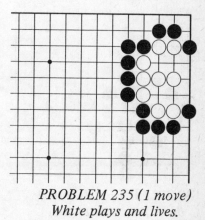

PROBLEM 235 (1 move)
White plays and lives.

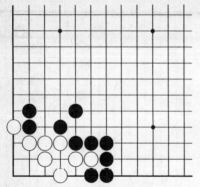

PROBLEM 236 (1 move)
Black plays White dies.

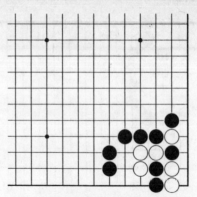

PROBLEM 237 (1 move)
Black plays White dies.

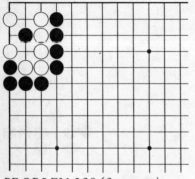

PROBLEM 238 (3 moves)
Black plays White dies.

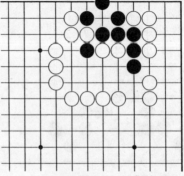

PROBLEM 239 (1 move)
Black plays and lives.

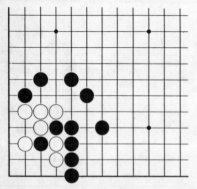

PROBLEM 240 (3 moves)
Black plays White dies.

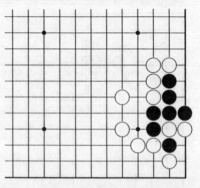

PROBLEM 241 (3 moves)
Black plays and lives.

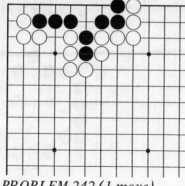

PROBLEM 242 (1 move)
Black plays and lives.

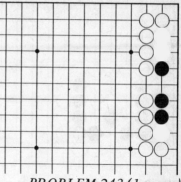

PROBLEM 243 (1 move)
Black plays and lives.

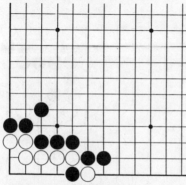
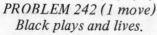

PROBLEM 244 (3 moves)
Black plays White dies.

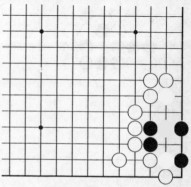

PROBLEM 245 (1 move)
Black plays and lives.

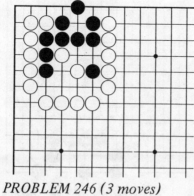

PROBLEM 246 (3 moves)
Black plays and lives.

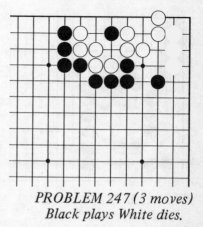

PROBLEM 247 (3 moves)
Black plays White dies.

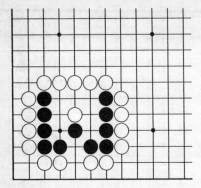

PROBLEM 248 (3 moves)
Black plays and lives.

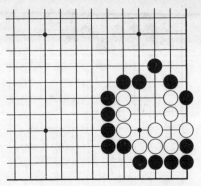

PROBLEM 249 (3 moves)
Black plays White dies.

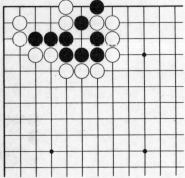

PROBLEM 250 (3 moves)
Black plays and lives.

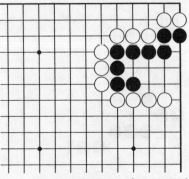

PROBLEM 251 (3 moves)
Black plays and lives.

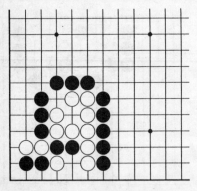

PROBLEM 252 (3 moves)
Black plays White dies.

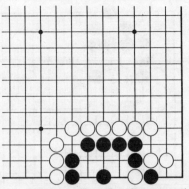

PROBLEM 253 (3 moves)
White plays Black dies.

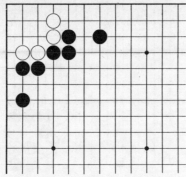

PROBLEM 254 (5 moves)
Black plays White dies.

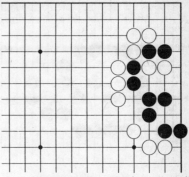

PROBLEM 255 (5 moves)
Black plays and lives.

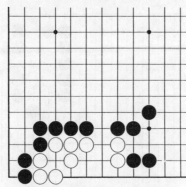

PROBLEM 256 (3 moves)
Black plays White dies.

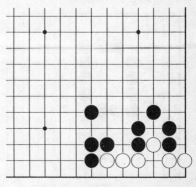

PROBLEM 257 (5 moves)
Black plays White dies.

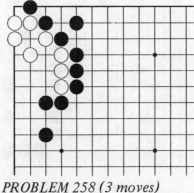

PROBLEM 258 (3 moves)
Black plays White dies.

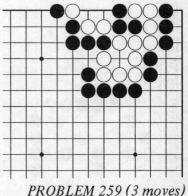

PROBLEM 259 (3 moves)
Black plays White dies.

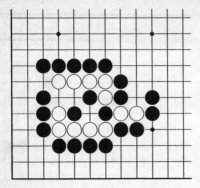

PROBLEM 260 (1 move)
White plays and lives.

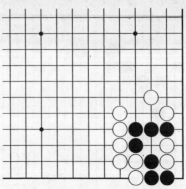

PROBLEM 261 (5 moves)
Black plays and lives.

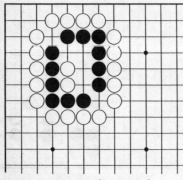

PROBLEM 262 (1 move)
White plays Black dies.

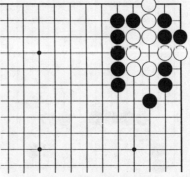

PROBLEM 263 (3 moves)
Black plays White dies.

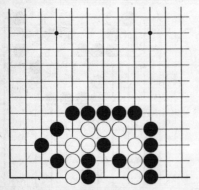

PROBLEM 264 (3 moves)
Black plays White dies.

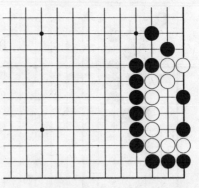

PROBLEM 265 (1 move)
Black plays White dies.

SECTION 2. KO

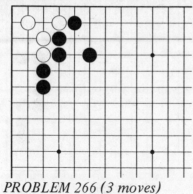

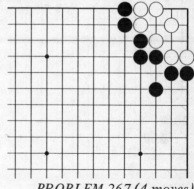

PROBLEM 266 (3 moves)
Black plays and makes a ko.

PROBLEM 267 (4 moves)
Black plays and makes a ko.

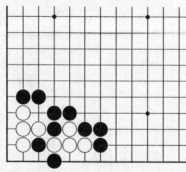

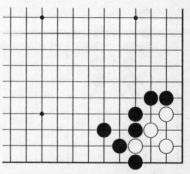

PROBLEM 268 (2 moves)
Black plays and makes a ko.

PROBLEM 269 (2 moves)
White plays and makes a ko.

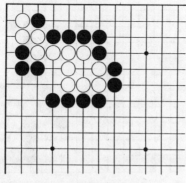

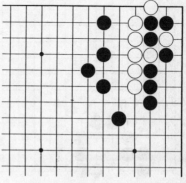

PROBLEM 270 (4 moves)
Black plays and makes a ko.

PROBLEM 271 (4 moves)
White plays and makes a ko.

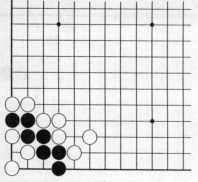

PROBLEM 272 (3 moves)
Black lives with a double ko.

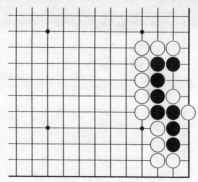

PROBLEM 273 (3 moves)
Black plays and lives.

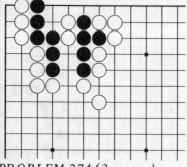

PROBLEM 274 (3 moves)
Black plays and lives.

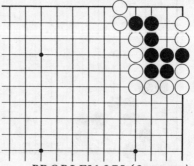

PROBLEM 275 (3 moves)
Black plays and lives.

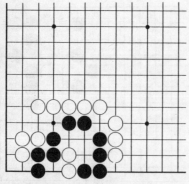

PROBLEM 276 (3 moves)
Black plays and lives.

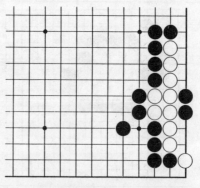

PROBLEM 277 (3 moves)
White plays and lives.

SECTION 4. CAPTURING RACES

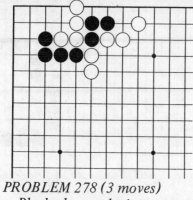

PROBLEM 278 (3 moves)
Black plays and wins.

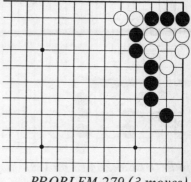

PROBLEM 279 (3 moves)
Black plays and wins.

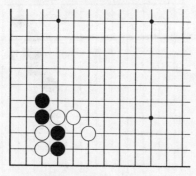

PROBLEM 280 (3 moves)
Black plays and wins.

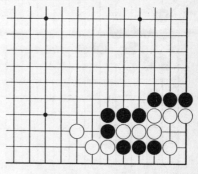

PROBLEM 281 (1 move)
Black plays and wins.

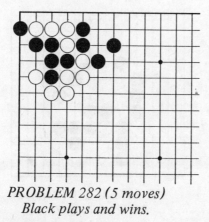

PROBLEM 282 (5 moves)
Black plays and wins.

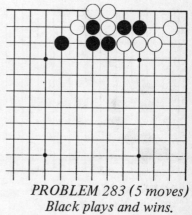

PROBLEM 283 (5 moves)
Black plays and wins.

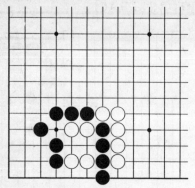

PROBLEM 284 (3 moves)
Black plays and wins.

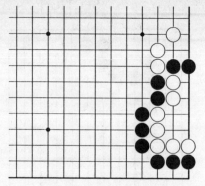

PROBLEM 285 (3 moves)
Black plays and wins.

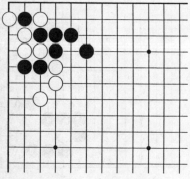

PROBLEM 286 (7 moves)
Black plays and wins.

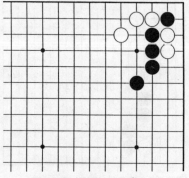

PROBLEM 287 (3 moves)
Black plays and wins.

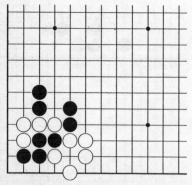

PROBLEM 288 (5 moves)
Black plays and wins.

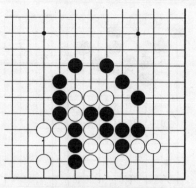

PROBLEM 289 (3 moves)
Black plays and wins.

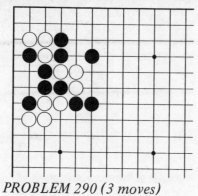

PROBLEM 290 (3 moves)
Black plays and wins.

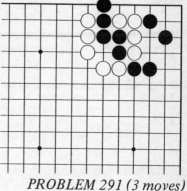

PROBLEM 291 (3 moves)
Black plays and wins.

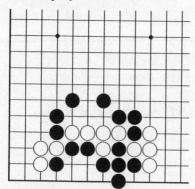

PROBLEM 292 (3 moves)
White plays and wins.

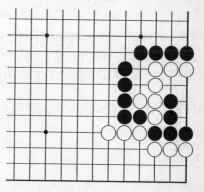

PROBLEM 293 (3 moves)
Black plays and wins.

IV INTERMEDIATE PROBLEMS
LEVEL FOUR
LIFE AND DEATH PROBLEMS

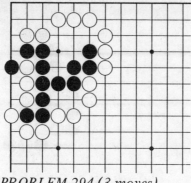

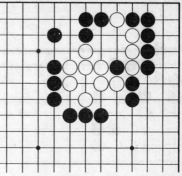

PROBLEM 294 (3 moves)
Black plays and lives.

PROBLEM 295 (1 move)
Black plays White dies.

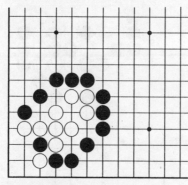

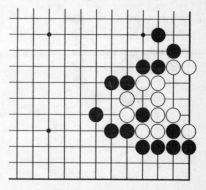

PROBLEM 296 (3 moves)
Black plays White dies.

PROBLEM 297 (3 moves)
Black plays White dies.

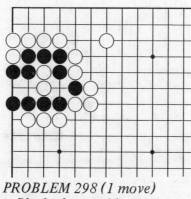

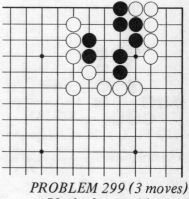

PROBLEM 298 (1 move)
Black plays and lives.

PROBLEM 299 (3 moves)
Black plays and lives.

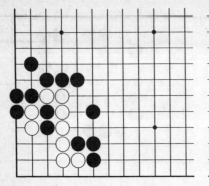

PROBLEM 300 (3 moves)
Black plays White dies.

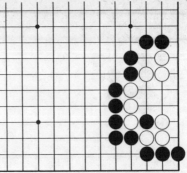

PROBLEM 301 (3 moves)
Black plays White dies.

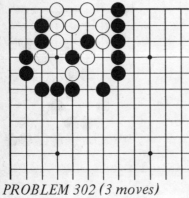

PROBLEM 302 (3 moves)
Black plays White dies.

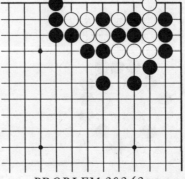

PROBLEM 303 (3 moves)
Black plays White dies.

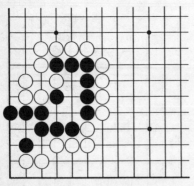

PROBLEM 304 (3 moves)
White plays and makes a ko.

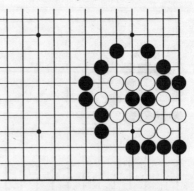

PROBLEM 305 (1 move)
Black plays White dies.

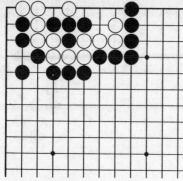

PROBLEM 306 (3 moves)
Black plays White dies.

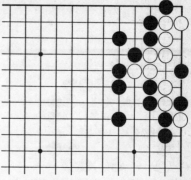

PROBLEM 307 (3 moves)
White plays and lives.

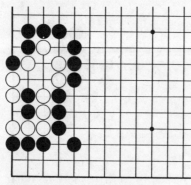

PROBLEM 308 (3 moves)
White plays and lives.

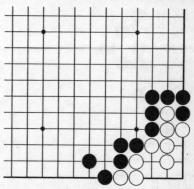

PROBLEM 309 (3 moves)
Black plays White dies.

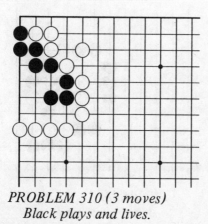

PROBLEM 310 (3 moves)
Black plays and lives.

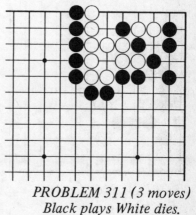

PROBLEM 311 (3 moves)
Black plays White dies.

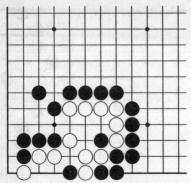

PROBLEM 312 (3 moves)
Black plays White dies.

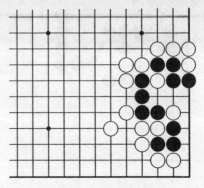

PROBLEM 313 (1 move)
Black plays and lives.

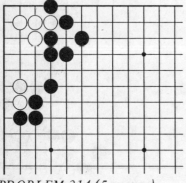

PROBLEM 314 (5 moves)
Black plays White dies.

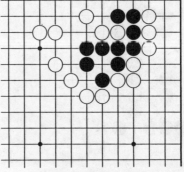

PROBLEM 315 (5 moves)
Black plays and lives.

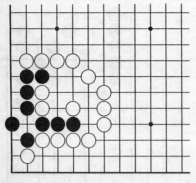

PROBLEM 316 (1 move)
Black plays and lives.

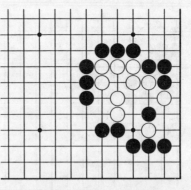

PROBLEM 317 (3 moves)
White plays and lives.

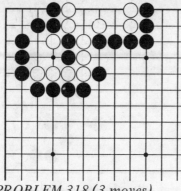

PROBLEM 318 (3 moves)
Black plays White dies.

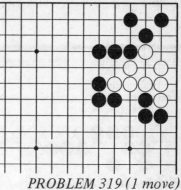

PROBLEM 319 (1 move)
White plays and lives.

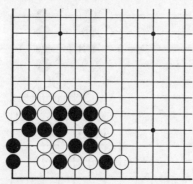

PROBLEM 320 (3 moves)
Black plays and lives.

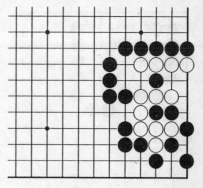

PROBLEM 321 (3 moves)
Black plays White dies.

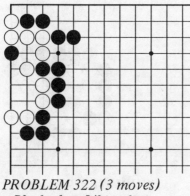

PROBLEM 322 (3 moves)
Black plays White dies.

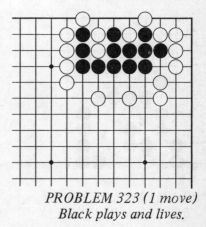

PROBLEM 323 (1 move)
Black plays and lives.

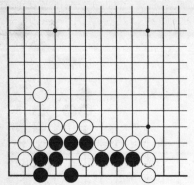

PROBLEM 324 (3 moves)
White plays Black dies.

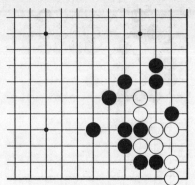

PROBLEM 325 (3 moves)
Black plays White dies.

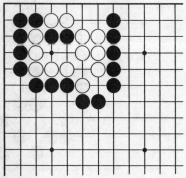

PROBLEM 326 (3 moves)
Black plays White dies.

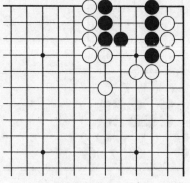

PROBLEM 327 (3 moves)
Black plays and lives.

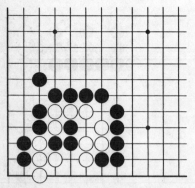

PROBLEM 328 (3 moves)
Black plays White dies.

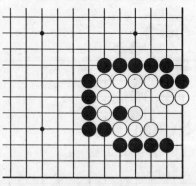

PROBLEM 329 (3 moves)
Black plays White dies.

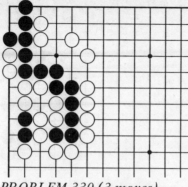

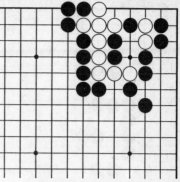

PROBLEM 330 (3 moves)
Black plays and lives.

PROBLEM 331 (1 move)
White plays and lives.

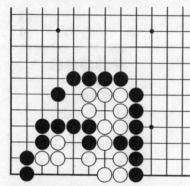

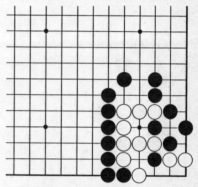

PROBLEM 332 (3 moves)
Black plays White dies.

PROBLEM 333 (3 moves)
Black plays White dies.

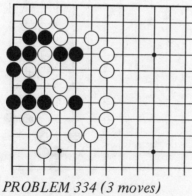

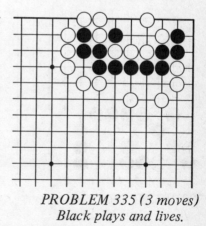

PROBLEM 334 (3 moves)
Black plays and lives.

PROBLEM 335 (3 moves)
Black plays and lives.

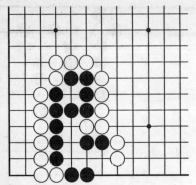

PROBLEM 336 (3 moves)
White plays Black dies.

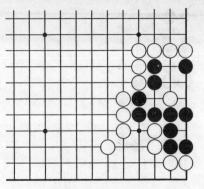

PROBLEM 337 (1 move)
White plays Black dies.

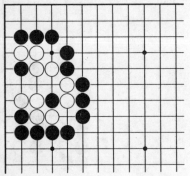

PROBLEM 338 (3 moves)
Black plays White dies.

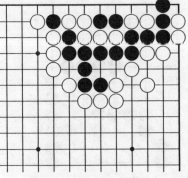

PROBLEM 339 (3 moves)
Black plays and lives.

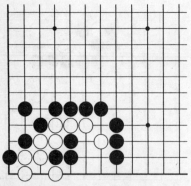

PROBLEM 340 (3 moves)
Black plays White dies.

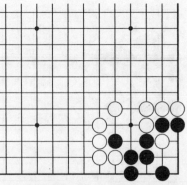

PROBLEM 341 (1 move)
Black plays and lives.

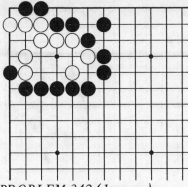

PROBLEM 342 (1 move)
White plays and lives.

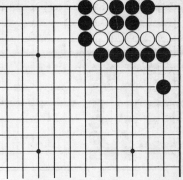

PROBLEM 343 (3 moves)
Black plays White dies.

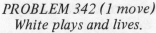
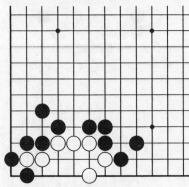

PROBLEM 344 (3 moves)
White plays and lives.

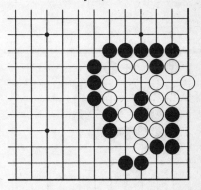

PROBLEM 345 (3 moves)
Black plays White dies.

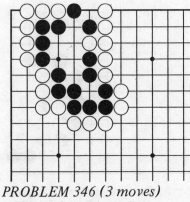

PROBLEM 346 (3 moves)
White plays Black dies.

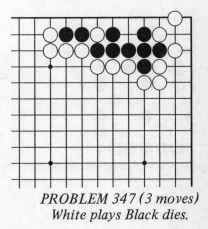

PROBLEM 347 (3 moves)
White plays Black dies.

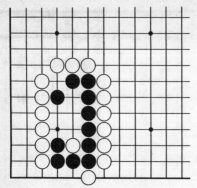

PROBLEM 348 (1 move)
Black plays and lives.

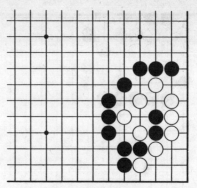

PROBLEM 349 (5 moves)
Black plays White dies.

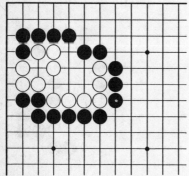

PROBLEM 350 (3 moves)
Black plays White dies.

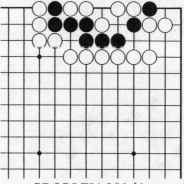

PROBLEM 351 (1 move)
Black plays and lives.

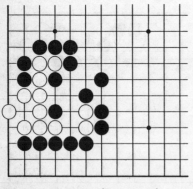

PROBLEM 352 (3 moves)
White plays and lives.

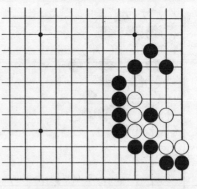

PROBLEM 353 (3 moves)
Black plays White dies.

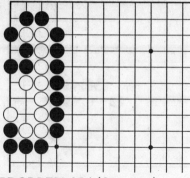

PROBLEM 354 (3 moves)
Black plays White dies.

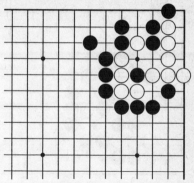

PROBLEM 355 (3 moves)
Black plays White dies.

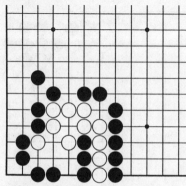

PROBLEM 356 (3 moves)
White plays and lives.

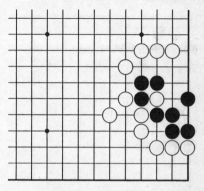

PROBLEM 357 (3 moves)
White plays Black dies.

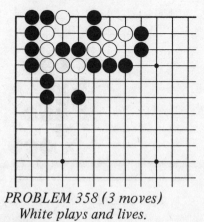

PROBLEM 358 (3 moves)
White plays and lives.

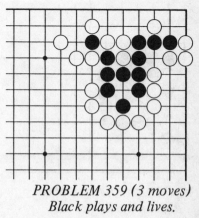

PROBLEM 359 (3 moves)
Black plays and lives.

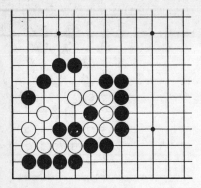

PROBLEM 360 (3 moves)
Black plays White dies.

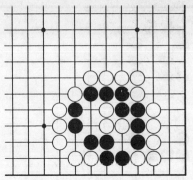

PROBLEM 361 (1 move)
Black plays and lives.

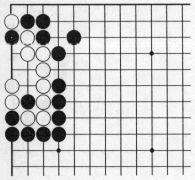

PROBLEM 362 (3 moves)
Black plays White dies.

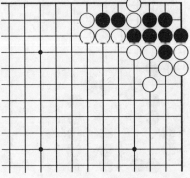

PROBLEM 363 (3 moves)
White plays Black dies.

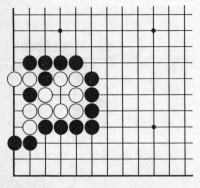

PROBLEM 364 (3 moves)
Black plays White dies.

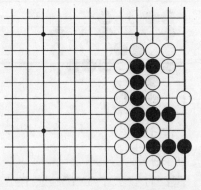

PROBLEM 365 (3 moves)
Black plays and lives.

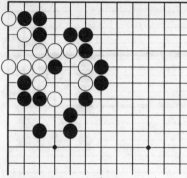

PROBLEM 366 (3 moves)
Black plays White dies.

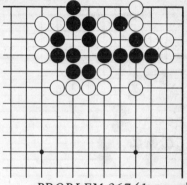

PROBLEM 367 (1 move)
White plays Black dies.

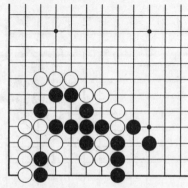

PROBLEM 368 (3 moves)
Black plays and lives.

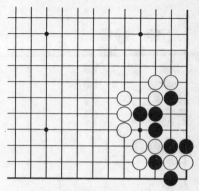

PROBLEM 369 (3 moves)
Black plays and lives.

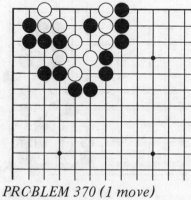

PROBLEM 370 (1 move)
White plays and lives.

PROBLEM 371 (3 moves)
Black plays White dies.

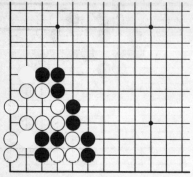

PROBLEM 372 (3 moves)
Black plays White dies.

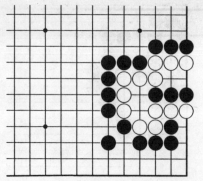

PROBLEM 373 (3 moves)
White plays and lives.

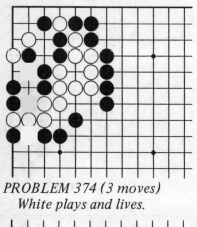

PROBLEM 374 (3 moves)
White plays and lives.

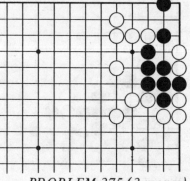

PROBLEM 375 (3 moves)
White plays Black dies.

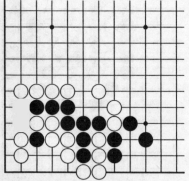

PROBLEM 376 (3 moves)
Black plays and lives.

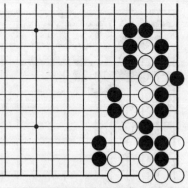

PROBLEM 377 (3 moves)
Black plays White dies.

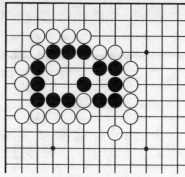

PROBLEM 378 (3 moves)
White plays Black dies.

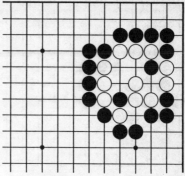

PROBLEM 379 (3 moves)
White plays and lives.

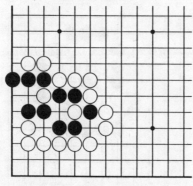

PROBLEM 380 (3 moves)
Black plays and lives.

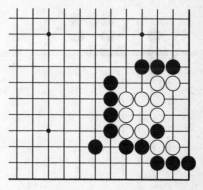

PROBLEM 381 (3 moves)
Black plays White dies.

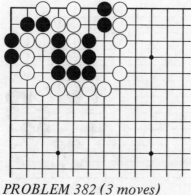

PROBLEM 382 (3 moves)
Black plays and lives.

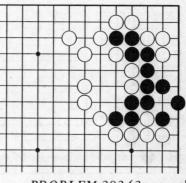

PROBLEM 383 (3 moves)
Black plays and lives.

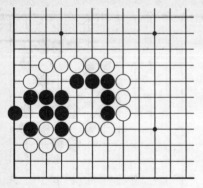

PROBLEM 384 (3 moves)
Black plays and lives.

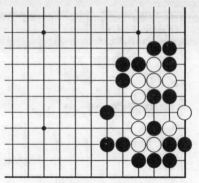

PROBLEM 385 (3 moves)
Black plays White dies.

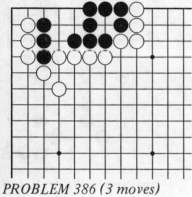

PROBLEM 386 (3 moves)
White plays Black dies.

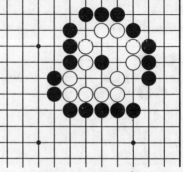

PROBLEM 387 (3 moves)
Black plays White dies.

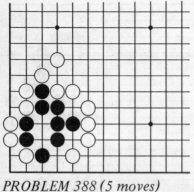

PROBLEM 388 (5 moves)
Black plays and lives.

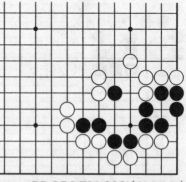

PROBLEM 389 (1 move)
Black plays and lives.

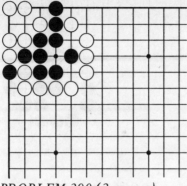

PROBLEM 390 (3 moves)
Black plays and lives.

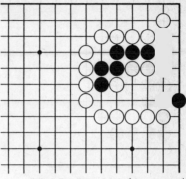

PROBLEM 391 (3 moves)
Black plays and lives.

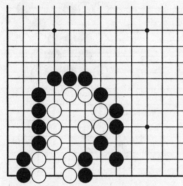

PROBLEM 392 (3 moves)
Black plays White dies.

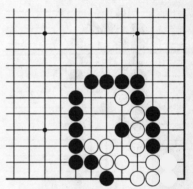

PROBLEM 393 (1 move)
White plays and lives.

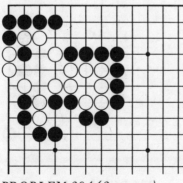

PROBLEM 394 (3 moves)
Black plays White dies.

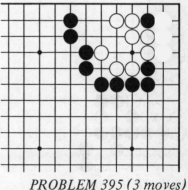

PROBLEM 395 (3 moves)
White plays and lives.

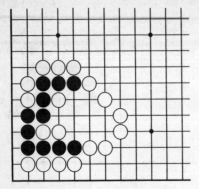

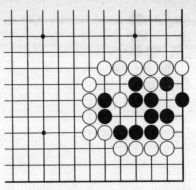

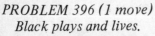

PROBLEM 396 (1 move)
Black plays and lives.

PROBLEM 397 (3 moves)
Black plays and lives.

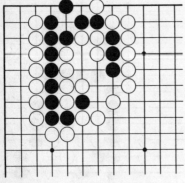

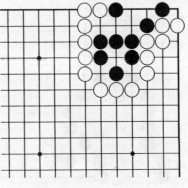

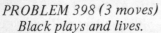

PROBLEM 398 (3 moves)
Black plays and lives.

PROBLEM 399 (1 move)
Black plays and lives.

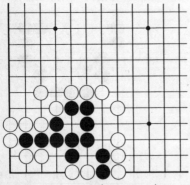

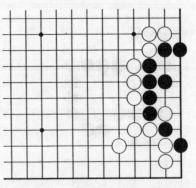

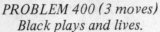

PROBLEM 400 (3 moves)
Black plays and lives.

PROBLEM 401 (2 moves)
Black plays and makes a ko.

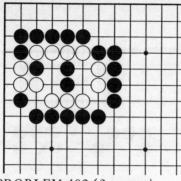

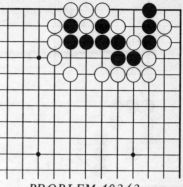

PROBLEM 402 (3 moves)
Black plays White dies.

PROBLEM 403 (3 moves)
Black plays and lives.

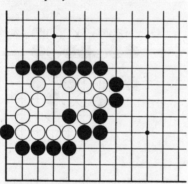

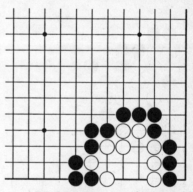

PROBLEM 404 (3 moves)
White plays and lives.

PROBLEM 405 (3 moves)
White plays and lives.

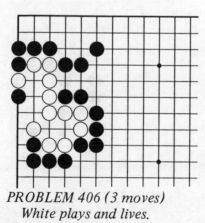

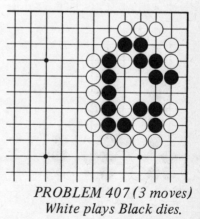

PROBLEM 406 (3 moves)
White plays and lives.

PROBLEM 407 (3 moves)
White plays Black dies.

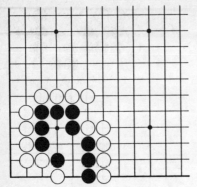

PROBLEM 408 (3 moves)
Black plays and lives.

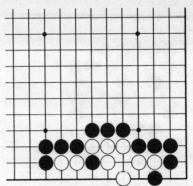

PROBLEM 409 (3 moves)
Black plays White dies.

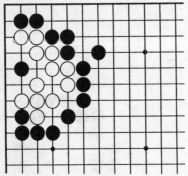

PROBLEM 410 (3 moves)
Black plays White dies.

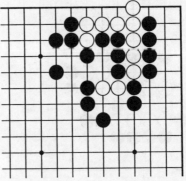

PROBLEM 411 (3 moves)
White plays and lives.

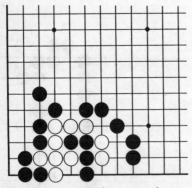

PROBLEM 412 (3 moves)
Black plays White dies.

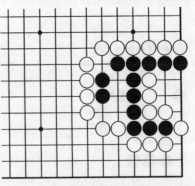

PROBLEM 413 (3 moves)
Black plays and lives.

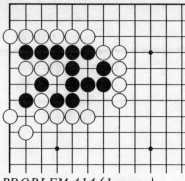

PROBLEM 414 (1 move)
Black plays and lives.

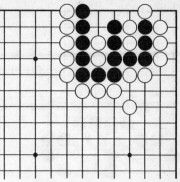

PROBLEM 415 (1 move)
White plays Black dies.

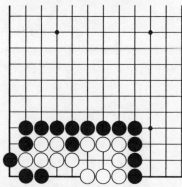

PROBLEM 416 (3 moves)
Black plays White dies.

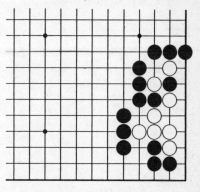

PROBLEM 417 (3 moves)
White plays and lives.

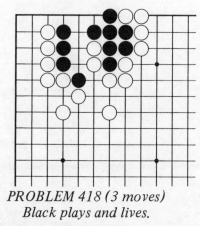

PROBLEM 418 (3 moves)
Black plays and lives.

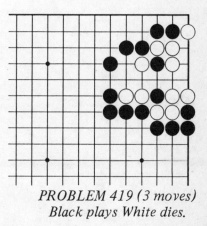

PROBLEM 419 (3 moves)
Black plays White dies.

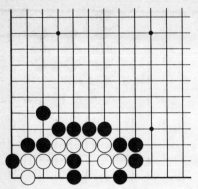

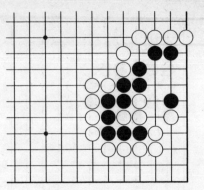

PROBLEM 420 (3 moves)
Black plays White dies.

PROBLEM 421 (3 moves)
Black plays and lives.

PART TWO

ANSWERS

PROBLEM 1

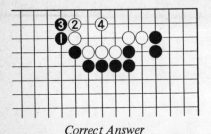

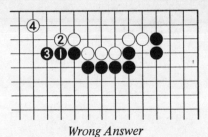

Correct Answer

Pressing from the outside with 1 and 3 is severe. White is confined to the side and must play 4 to live.

Wrong Answer

Extending to 1 is slack; White expands along the side with 2 and 4. This is a failure for Black.

PROBLEM 2

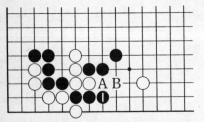

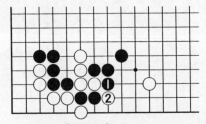

Correct Answer

Black saves his two stones by extending to 1. If White A, Black blocks at B and Black cannot be captured.

Wrong Answer

If Black blocks at 1, White catches two black stones when he ataris at 2.

PROBLEM 3

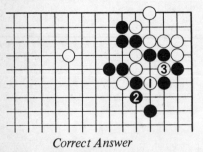

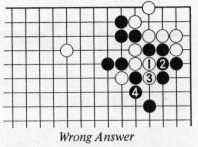

Correct Answer

White can escape if he ataris at 1. If Black 2, White captures two stones with 3. If Black 2 at 3, White 3 at 2.

Wrong Answer

Directly playing atari with 1 is crude. After the sequence to 4, White's four stones are lost.

PROBLEM 4

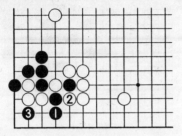

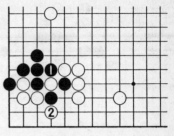

Correct Answer

Descending to 1, followed by 3, catches three white stones in the corner.

Wrong Answer

Capturing with 1 allows White to link up his stones on the left to the ones on the right.

PROBLEM 5

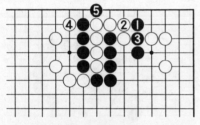

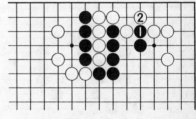

Correct Answer

If Black places a stone at 1, Black wins the capturing race by one move. If White 2 at 3, Black 3 at 2.

Wrong Answer

Pushing through with 1 only helps White to link up his stones. The four black stones on the left are now dead.

PROBLEM 6

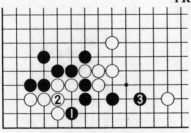

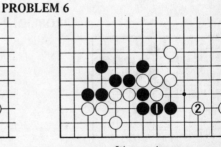

Correct Answer

First of all, Black plays 1, threatening to capture two stones with 2. When White defends, Black extends to 3.

Wrong Answer

If Black 1, Black's stones are in a pinch after White 2. If Black 2, White plays 1, capturing two black stones.

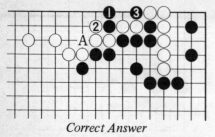

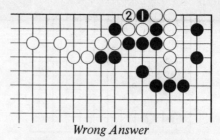

Correct Answer

Black 1 sets up a throw-in at 3 which captures two stones. If White 2 at 3, Black cuts at A, capturing two white stones.

Wrong Answer

Throwing in first at 1 is premature. The lone black stone on the left will be captured before the white stones on the right.

PROBLEM 8

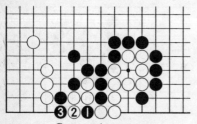

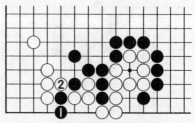

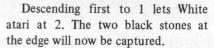

Correct Answer

Exchanging 1 for 2 lets Black atari at 3 in sente. The white group on the right is now isolated with only one eye.

Wrong Answer

Descending first to 1 lets White atari at 2. The two black stones at the edge will now be captured.

PROBLEM 9

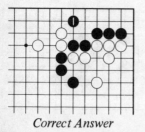

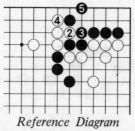

Correct Answer

Black 1 is the 'shape' move that gives Black's group in the corner life. Next —

Reference Diagram

White 2 and 4 are the best White can do. Up to 5, Black gets a living shape in the corner.

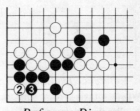

Wrong Answer 1

If Black 1, White 2 aims at 3. Up to 6, the situation is either seki or ko. This is a big loss for Black.

Wrong Answer 2

Black 1 is the worst move. White 2 and 4 kill the black group.

PROBLEM 10

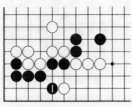

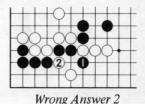

Correct Answer

Black 1 is the best move in this position. Next —

Reference Diagram

If White attacks at 2, Black 3 gives the black group in the corner two eyes.

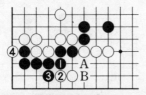

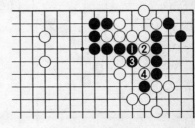

Wrong Answer 1

If Black 1, White kills Black with 2 and 4. If Black A next, White B.

Wrong Answer 2

Black 1 is unreasonable. When White cuts at 2, Black loses three stones.

PROBLEM 11

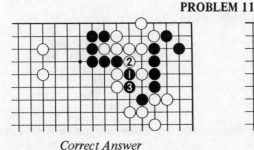

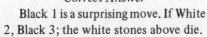

Correct Answer

Black 1 is a surprising move. If White 2, Black 3; the white stones above die.

Wrong Answer

Black 1 is artless. Up to 4, White links up to his stones on the outside.

PROBLEM 12

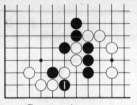

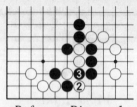

Correct Answer

Cutting with Black 1 is the correct move. White will now lose two stones.

Reference Diagram 1

If White ataris with 2, Black 3 will capture the two stones in atari.

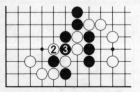

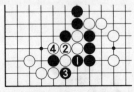

Reference Diagram 2

If White ataris from the outside with 2, Black 3 again will capture two white stones.

Wrong Answer

Directly giving atari to the two white stones without first cutting leads to failure, as this diagrams shows.

PROBLEM 13

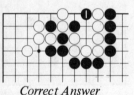

Correct Answer

After Black 1, White can't give atari to the two black stones, so seven white ones can be captured.

Wrong Answer

Black 1 and 3 lead to a seki. However, if Black 1 at 3, White plays 2 at 1 and Black will be captured.

PROBLEM 14

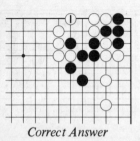

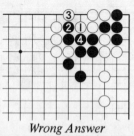

Correct Answer

White can link up his three stones with 1.

Wrong Answer

White 1 fails. After Black 2 and 4, White's stones cannot escape atari.

PROBLEM 15

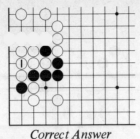

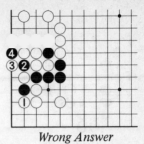

Correct Answer

If White connects at 1, his six stones at the edge cannot be captured.

Wrong Answer

If White 1, Black throws in a stone at 2. After 4, White loses four stones.

PROBLEM 16

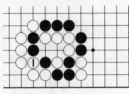

Correct Answer

White 1 ensures that six black stones will be captured.

Wrong Answer

If White ataris with 1, Black 2 will capture five white stones.

PROBLEM 17

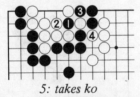

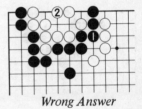

5: takes ko
Correct Answer

Black can get an advantageous ko by throwing in a stone at 1.

Wrong Answer

If Black connects at 1, White gets two real eyes by playing at 2.

PROBLEM 18

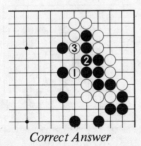

Correct Answer

If White ataris with 1, Black's five stones can't escape capture. If Black 2, White 3.

Wrong Answer

White 1 only threatens two unimportant stones. Black connects with 2, catching four white stones.

PROBLEM 19

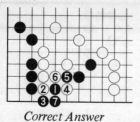

Correct Answer

Black 1 ensures a connection between the two black groups.

Wrong Answer

Black cannot link up with 1 and 3. White 4 ensures the separation.

PROBLEM 20

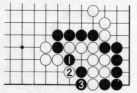

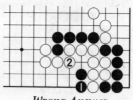

Correct Answer

Black cuts at 1. If White ataris with 2, Black 3 sets up a snapback.

Wrong Answer

If Black 1, White secures his stones by connecting at 2.

PROBLEM 21

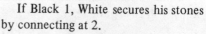

Correct Answer

Black 1 is the point to attack. Up to 3, it is clear that White's stones die.

Wrong Answer

If Black captures with 1, he loses the capturing race by one move.

PROBLEM 22

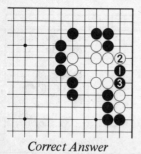

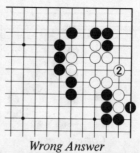

Correct Answer

Black 1 is the vital point. If White 2, Black 3. If White 2 at 3, Black 3 at 2.

Wrong Answer

If Black 1, White will play on the vital point himself and live.

PROBLEM 23

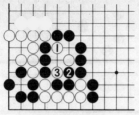

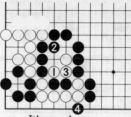

Correct Answer

White 1 and 3 allow White to link up all his stones and live.

Wrong Answer

White 1 and 3 capture two stones, but 4 takes away White's second eye.

PROBLEM 24

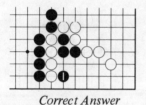

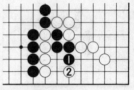

Correct Answer

Black 1 is the vital point to capture the four white stones.

Wrong Answer

Black 1 fails. Against White 2, Black has no answer.

PROBLEM 25

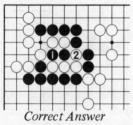

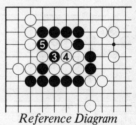

Correct Answer

Sacrificing two stones with Black 1 is the way to capture White's stones.

Reference Diagram

Black sacrifices another stone with 3 and gives the killing atari with 5.

PROBLEM 26

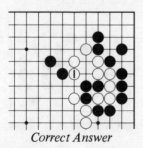

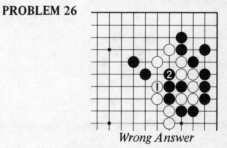

Correct Answer

After White 1, the three black stones cannot escape.

Wrong Answer

Giving atari with 1 is a crude move. Black escapes with 2.

PROBLEM 27

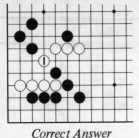

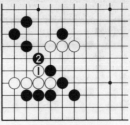

Correct Answer

White 1 makes the linkup between the two white groups.

Wrong Answer

If White 1, Black blocks with 2. Now White's stones on the left are dead.

PROBLEM 28

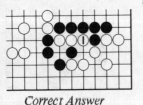

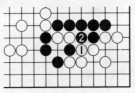

Correct Answer

There is no way for Black to capture White after he plays 1.

Wrong Answer

If White ataris with 1, Black sets up a snapback with 2. White has failed.

PROBLEM 29

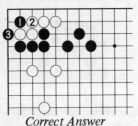

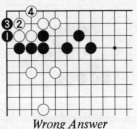

Correct Answer

Black 1 is the vital point. After 3, there is no way for White to live.

Wrong Answer

If Black 1, White gets two eyes with 2 and 4. Black has failed.

PROBLEM 30

Correct Answer

Black can kill the white group with a throw-in at 1, followed by 3.

Wrong Answer

Without the sacrifice, Black would lose his three stones on the right.

PROBLEM 31

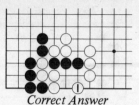

Correct Answer

White 1 saves his four stones on the left. Now Black's three stones are dead.

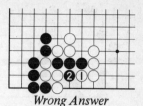

Wrong Answer

White 1 fails. Black will capture four white stones after playing 2.

PROBLEM 32

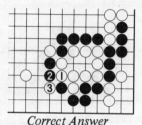

Correct Answer

After White 1 and 3, all the black stones at the edge will die.

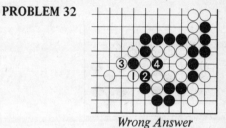

Wrong Answer

If White 1, Black will capture eight white stones with 2 and 4.

PROBLEM 33

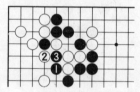

Correct Answer

Black 1 and 3 capture three white stones and save Black's at the top.

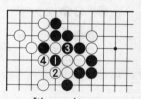

Wrong Answer

If Black captures a stone with 1 and 3, his stones at the top will die.

PROBLEM 34

Correct Answer

Black 1 and 3 catch the five white stones on the left.

Wrong Answer

Black 1 and 3 are thoughtless moves. After 4, all White's stones are safe.

PROBLEM 35

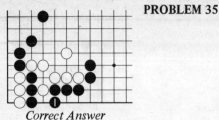

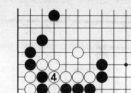

Correct Answer

Black 1 saves his three stones to the left by defending against oiotoshi.

Wrong Answer

If Black ataris at 1, White 2 and 4 set up an oiotoshi.

PROBLEM 36

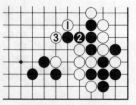

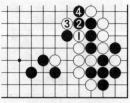

Correct Answer

White 1 and 3 catch four of Black's stones.

Wrong Answer

White 1 and 3 here fail to capture any black stones.

PROBLEM 37

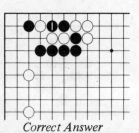

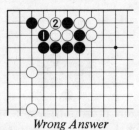

Correct Answer

If Black plays at 1, he will capture three white stones.

Wrong Answer

Black 1 is in the wrong direction. Black fails to capture any stones.

PROBLEM 38

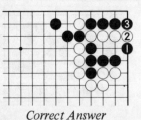

Correct Answer

Black 1 and 3 are the only moves that will catch White's stones.

Wrong Answer

If Black plays 1 and 3, White cannot be captured after White 2 and 4.

PROBLEM 39

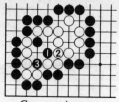

Correct Answer

Black 1 and 3 set up a snapback. All of White's stones will die.

Wrong Answer

If Black ataris at 1, he has no follow-up after White 2.

PROBLEM 40

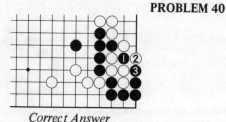

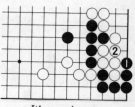

Correct Answer

Black sacrifices a stone and then ataris at 3. White cannot escape.

Wrong Answer

If Black simply ataris at 1, Black has no follow-up after White 2.

PROBLEM 41

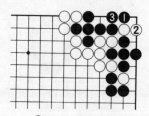

Correct Answer

If Black makes an eye with 1 and 3, he can eventually capture two stones.

Wrong Answer

If Black ataris with 1, he will lose his five stones at the top after White 2.

PROBLEM 42

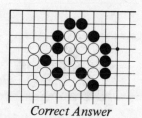

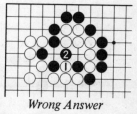

Correct Answer

White 1 is the only move that will save his endangered stones.

Wrong Answer

If White 1, Black 2 sets up a snapback. Black 2 is the vital point.

PROBLEM 43

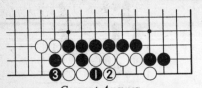

Correct Answer

If Black sacrifices a stone with 1, White can't escape capture after 3.

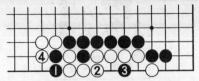

Wrong Answer

If Black simply ataris with 1, he loses the capturing race by one move.

PROBLEM 44

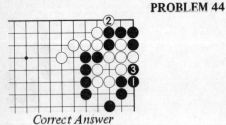

Correct Answer

If Black starts the attack from the side, he will capture White.

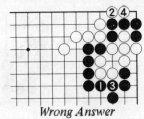

Wrong Answer

If Black plays 1 and 3 from below, he loses his five stones at the top.

PROBLEM 45

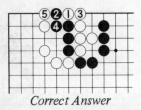

Correct Answer

White 1 is the vital point. White wins the capturing race by one move.

Wrong Answer

If White 1 here, White loses the capturing race by one move.

PROBLEM 46

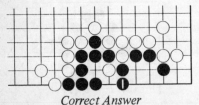

Correct Answer

Black has to play 1 if his stones at the bottom are going to live.

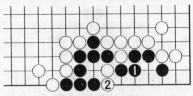

Wrong Answer

If Black connects at 1, White 2 catches eight black stones.

PROBLEM 47

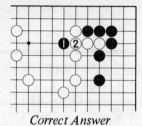

Correct Answer

Peeping at 1 is a bad move. The reasons are given in the next diagrams.

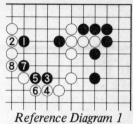

Reference Diagram 1

It is practically impossible for Black to live. If he tries, White gets thickness.

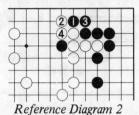

Reference Diagram 2

After peeping, the best endgame moves are Black 1 and 3.

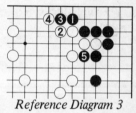

Reference Diagram 3

Without the peep, Black has more profitable endgame moves up to 5.

PROBLEM 48

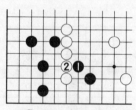

Correct Answer

Peeping at 1 is a bad move. The reasons are given in the next diagrams.

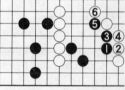

Reference Diagram 1

The thickness White gets if Black tries to live is too good.

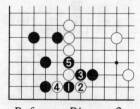

Reference Diagram 2

Without the peep, Black would be able to link up to his stones on the left.

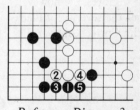

Reference Diagram 3

It is impossible for White to prevent this linkage, as the sequence to 5 shows.

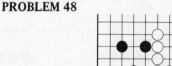

PROBLEM 49

Correct Answer

There are a lot of places that Black would like to play, but Black 1 here (D in the Problem Diagram) is the best point. The reason is that Black 1 creates two weak white groups: the four stones at the top and the eleven in the center.

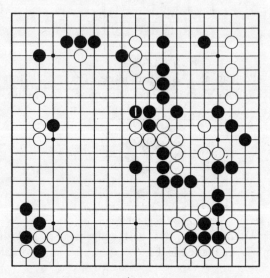

Wrong Answers

Black 1 is a big move, worth more than ten points. Black 2 is also big and Black would like to play there as soon as possible. Black 3 is not bad either, but it is in the wrong direction. None of these moves, however, matches the severity of Black 1 in the Correct Answer diagram.

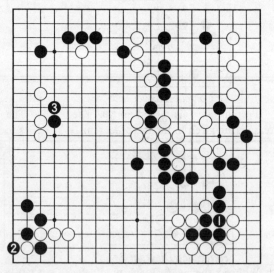

PROBLEM 50

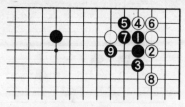

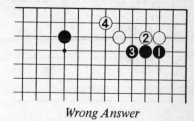

Correct Answer

Because of the black stone under the star-point to the left, blocking at 1 is the best move. The sequence to Black 9 is a basic joseki. The stone to the left is now an ideal extension from the black formation on the right.

Wrong Answer

If Black blocks from the other side with 1 as here, the black stone under the star-point is out of place after the continuation to 4.

PROBLEM 51

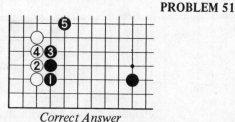

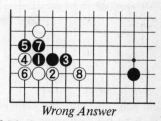

Correct Answer

'Build a wall on the side that you have a stone on or near the star-point.' The moves Black 1, 3 and 5 follow this principle.

Wrong Answer

If Black makes a wall in the other direction, the stone under the star-point is out of place after White 8.

PROBLEM 52

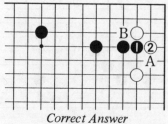

Correct Answer

In this position, blocking at 1 is played in almost all cases. After White 2 Black has the choice of playing at either A or B.

Wrong Answer

Blocking at 1 makes it easy for White to link up his stones with 2. Territorially, Black has suffered a big loss.

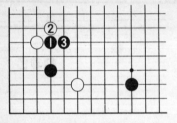

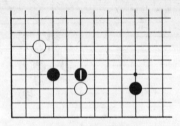

Correct Answer

'When confronted with a double-approach move, always attach against the stone which is not attacked by a pincer.' Black 1 follows this principle.

Reference Diagram

Attaching at 1 on the side that you have a pincer (the black stone under the star-point) is a strategy for special situations.

PROBLEM 54

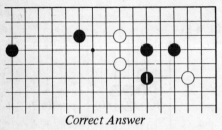

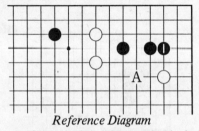

Correct Answer

Jumping out into the center with Black 1 is a standard move in handicap games.

Reference Diagram

Defending the corner with Black 1 is another move that can be considered, but Black 1 at A is bad shape. There are other moves, but Black 1 in the correct answer is superior to all of them.

PROBLEM 55

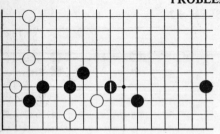

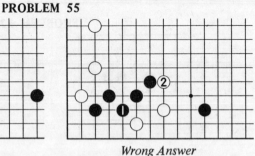

Correct Answer

Confining White to the side with Black 1 is the best move. Even if you fail to kill White, you cannot get a bad result.

Wrong Answer

Black 1 is a cowardly move. White easily moves out into the center with 2 and Black's stones in the corner are overconcentrated.

Correct Answer

Capping the four white stones with Black 1 is the most important move on the board. It is impossible to estimate how profitable this move is.

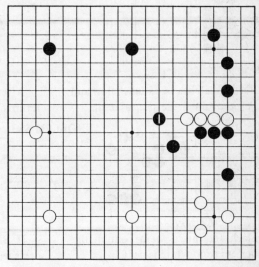

Wrong Answer

No one can say that Black 1 is a bad move, but attacking the four white stones on the right as in the Correct Answer is far more profitable.

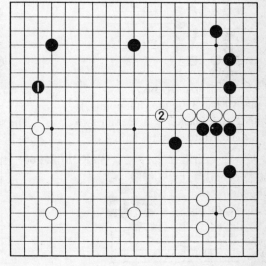

PROBLEM 57

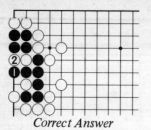

Correct Answer

Black 1 catches one stone below and sets up the 'under the stones' tesuji.

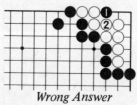

Reference Diagram

After White captures at 2, Black 3 returns to capture two white stones.

PROBLEM 58

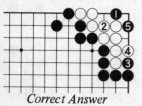

Correct Answer

Black sets up a 'bent four in the corner' up to 5. White is dead.

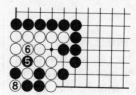

Wrong Answer

If Black ataris with 1, White connects with 2. White cannot be killed.

PROBLEM 59

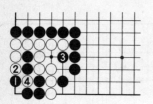

Correct Answer

Black 1 and 3 are the vital points. If White 2 at 3, Black 3 at 2, making two eyes. After White captures with 4 —

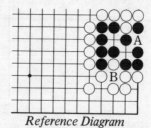

7: connects; 9: below 5
Reference Diagram

The sequence to 8 leaves White with a dead 6-space big eye. 9 kills White.

PROBLEM 60

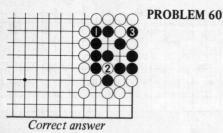

Correct answer

Black 1 is the vital point. If White 2, Black 3. Black lives because of the double ko.

Reference Diagram

If White makes a ko threat, then takes at A, Black simply takes at B.

PROBLEM 61

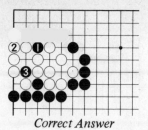

Correct Answer

Black 1 is the vital point. If 2, Black 3 kills White. White gets only one eye.

Wrong Answer

If Black 1, White plays the vital point and easily gets two eyes.

PROBLEM 62

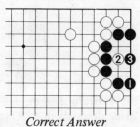

Correct Answer

Black 1 makes the 'comb formation', a standard living shape. If 2, Black 3.

Wrong Answer

If Black 1, White can get a ko with the atari of 2.

PROBLEM 63

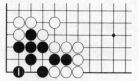

Correct Answer

Black 1 makes two eyes. If White takes two stones, Black retakes.

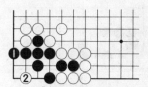

Wrong Answer

If Black 1, White plays on the vital point of 2 and Black dies.

PROBLEM 64

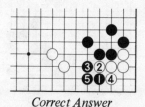

Correct Answer

Black 1 is the vital point. No matter how White plays, he can't get two eyes.

Wrong Answer

If Black simply plays 1, White lives by playing 2 and 4.

PROBLEM 65

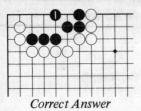

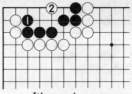

Correct Answer

Black 1 is the vital point for making eye shape. With 1, Black easily lives.

Wrong Answer

If Black 1, White 2 kills the black group.

PROBLEM 66

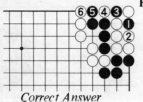

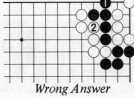

Correct Answer

Black 1 and 3 are the right order of moves. After 6, it is Black's turn to take the ko.

Wrong Answer

If Black descends to 1, White plays 2. Since White's group has an eye, Black loses the capturing race.

PROBLEM 67

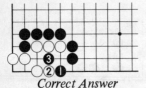

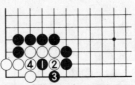

Correct Answer

Black 1 is the vital point. White cannot capture 3, so he is dead.

Wrong Answer

If Black 1, White lives by playing 2 and 4.

PROBLEM 68

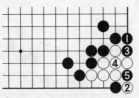

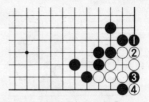

Correct Answer 1

Black 1 is the vital point for getting a ko. White 2 is one of two variations.

Correct Answer 2

White could also play 2 as here. The result is again a ko.

PROBLEM 69

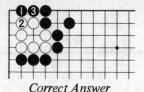

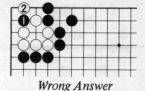

Correct Answer

Black 1 is the vital point. If White 2, Black 3 and White dies.

Wrong Answer

If Black 1, White lives by playing at 2.

PROBLEM 70

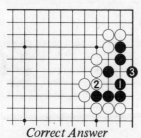

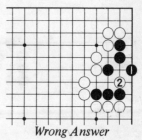

Correct Answer

Black 1 is the vital point. If 2, Black 3. If White 2 at 3, Black 3 at 2.

Wrong Answer

Black 1 is refuted by White 2, the vital point. Black dies.

PROBLEM 71

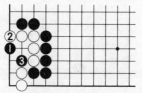

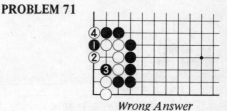

Correct Answer

Black plays 1 and 3. Because of shortage of liberties, White cannot attack the two black stones, so he dies.

Wrong Answer

Black 1, followed by 3, fails. After 4, White has no trouble making life.

PROBLEM 72

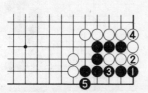

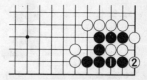

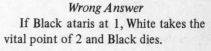

Correct Answer

Black 1 forces White 2. Black can now get two eyes with 3 and 5.

Wrong Answer

If Black ataris at 1, White takes the vital point of 2 and Black dies.

PROBLEM 73

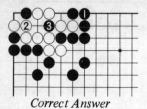

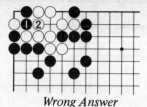

Correct Answer

Black 1 is the vital point for attack. If White 2, Black 3 kills White.

Wrong Answer

If Black 1, White catches these two stones and gets two eyes.

PROBLEM 74

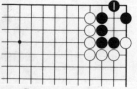

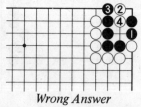

Correct Answer

Black 1 is the vital point for getting two eyes.

Wrong Answer

If Black ataris with 1, White plays 2, followed by 4, and Black dies.

PROBLEM 75

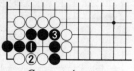

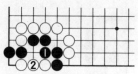

Correct Answer

Black 1 and 3 are the vital points. The result is a seki.

Wrong Answer

If Black ataris with 1, he is dead after White plays 2.

PROBLEM 76

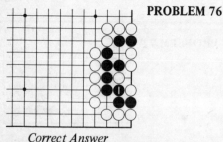

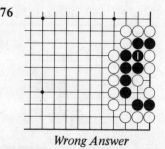

Correct Answer

Black 1 sets up an oiotoshi. Black loses two stones, but he still lives.

Wrong Answer

If Black plays at 1, he is dead as he stands.

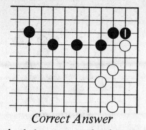

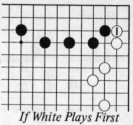

Correct Answer

Black 1 is among the biggest end-game moves.

If White Plays First

If it were White's turn, this is where he would play.

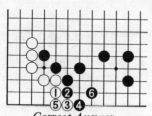

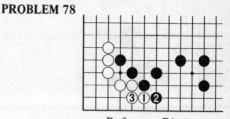

Correct Answer

White 1, followed by 3 and 5, is sente and the best endgame sequence.

Reference Diagram

Actually White 1 and 3 are more profitable, but this sequence ends in gote.

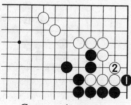

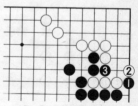

Correct Answer

Black 1 is best. After White 2, Black will play elsewhere.

Reference Diagram

White 2 is unreasonable. Black will capture three white stones with 3.

Wrong Answer 1

Black 1 is crude. In the sequence to 7, Black ends in gote.

Wrong Answer 2

Black 1 has the same value as the correct answer, but A becomes sente for White.

PROBLEM 80

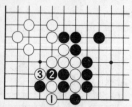

Correct Answer

White 1 prevents Black from linking up with his lone stone on the left.

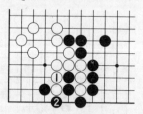

Continuation

After White 1, the sequence will continue up to Black 4.

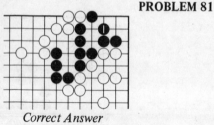

Reference Diagram

Black 2 is unreasonable. White 3 catches three black stones.

Wrong Answer

White 1 lets Black link up his stones. This is a big loss in territory for White.

PROBLEM 81

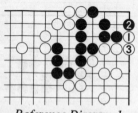

Correct Answer

Black 1 is the correct answer. The reasons are given in the next diagrams.

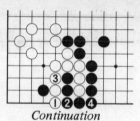

Wrong Answer

If Black 1, White can play 2 and 4 in sente.

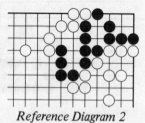

Reference Diagram 1

In the correct answer, White 1 and 3 end in gote for White.

Reference Diagram 2

Using this diagram for analysis, Black has 7 points, whereas in the Wrong Answer Diagram he has only 5 points.

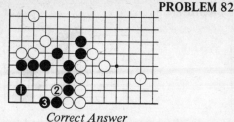

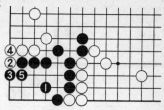

Correct Answer

Black 1 is the correct answer. Even if White cuts at 2, Black need not worry.

Wrong Answer

If Black 1, White can play 2 and 4 in sente. This is a 4-point loss for Black.

PROBLEM 83

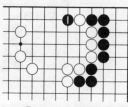

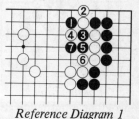

Correct Answer

Black 1 causes a huge reduction in White's territory.

Reference Diagram 1

Resisting with 2 is unreasonable, as the sequence to Black 7 shows.

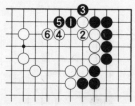

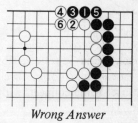

Reference Diagram 2

White must prudently play 2. However, Black has made a big invasion.

Wrong Answer

Ordinary endgame moves up to Black 5 allow White to keep his territory intact.

PROBLEM 84

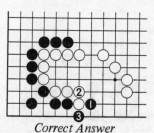

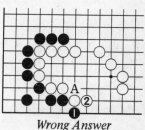

Correct Answer

A clamp with Black 1 is again the right way to invade White's territory.

Wrong Answer

Neither Black 1 nor A is a very big endgame move. White replies with 2.

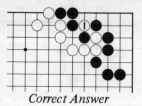

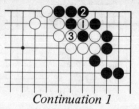

Correct Answer

Throwing in a stone with White 1 is the correct answer. Next —

Continuation 1

Because of shortage of liberties, taking with 2 is the only move. After 3 —

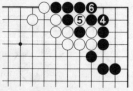

Continuation 2

To avoid an unfavorable ko, Black must defend with 4 and 6.

Wrong Answer

If White exchanges 1 for 2, Black's territory here is at least 3 points more than in the preceding diagram.

PROBLEM 86

Correct Answer

Black 1 and 3, followed by 5, are the best endgame moves. Black retains sente after White connects with 6.

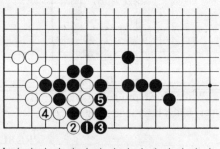

Wrong Answer

Black also retains sente with this sequence, but it is two points better for White.

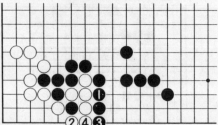

PROBLEM 87

Correct Answer

Black 1 sets up a double threat. He can capture two stones by playing at either 2 or 3.

Wrong Answer

Black 1 is the wrong order of moves. After White 2, Black has no follow-up.

PROBLEM 88

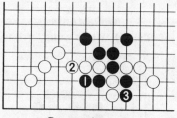

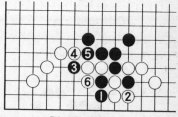

Correct Answer

Black 1 again sets up a double threat. He can capture two stones by playing at either 2 or 3.

Wrong Answer

Black 1 is the wrong order of moves. After White 2, no matter how Black plays, he cannot capture any stones.

PROBLEM 89

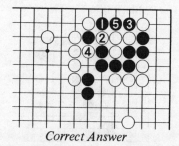

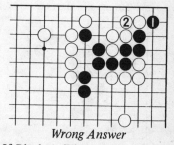

Correct Answer

Black plays 1 and then squeezes up to 5. Black can now take the white stone in the corner.

Wrong Answer

If Black 1, White connects at 2 and Black loses both territory and eye shape in the corner.

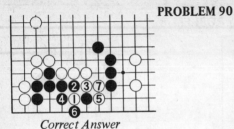

Correct Answer

If White cuts at 1, he succeeds in splitting Black in two up to 7.

Wrong Answer

If White 1, Black can link up his stones with the sequence to 4.

PROBLEM 91

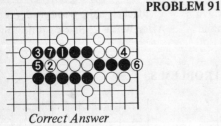

Correct Answer

By squeezing up to 7, Black gets a strong wall on the outside.

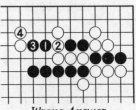

Wrong Answer

If Black 1, White gains territory at the top.

PROBLEM 92

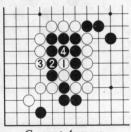

Correct Answer

First of all, White increases the sacrifice to two stones and starts to squeeze.

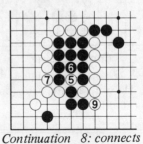

Continuation 8: connects

The squeeze continues up to 8. After 9, Black is in trouble.

Wrong Answer 1

If White 1 immediately, Black captures with 2 and Black's stones are safe.

Wrong Answer 2

An atari from the left with White 1 is similar to the preceding diagram.

PROBLEM 93

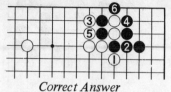

Correct Answer

White 1, followed by 3 and 5, is the right order of moves.

Wrong Answer

If White 3, Black exchanges 4 for 5, leaving a cutting point at A for later.

PROBLEM 94

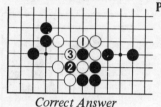

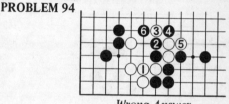

Correct Answer

White takes care of his stones with 1 and 3 and gets good shape.

Wrong Answer

If White connects at 1, Black divides White into two weak groups.

PROBLEM 95

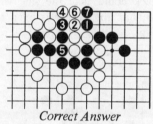

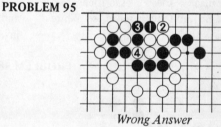

Correct Answer

Black can capture the three white stones up to 7. White cannot escape.

Wrong Answer

Black 1 and 3 fail. White ataris with 4 and the three black stones die.

PROBLEM 96

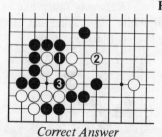

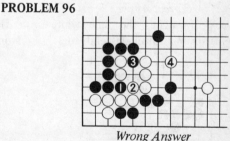

Correct Answer

Because White can't make eyes he has to jump to 2 when Black plays 1. Next, 3 cuts off five white stones.

Wrong Answer

Black 1 lets White connect at the vital point of 2. Black 3 takes away the second eye, but White escape with 4.

PROBLEM 97

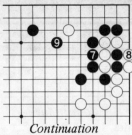

Correct Answer

Black increases the sacrifice to two stones and then squeezes with 3 and 5.

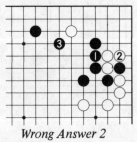

Continuation

Black 7 seals White in, and Black 9 takes the territory at the top.

Wrong Answer 1

If Black doesn't sacrifice two stones, he can't keep sente, so White escapes with 4.

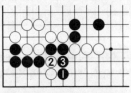

Wrong Answer 2

Black could take the side with 1 and 3, but the corner is open to an invasion.

PROBLEM 98

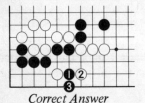

Correct Answer

Black 1 catches the lone white stone. If White 2, Black descends to 3.

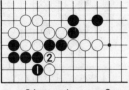

Reference Diagram

If White plays 2, he just loses two stones after Black 3.

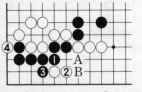

Wrong Answer 1

If Black connects at 1, he is dead after White 2 and 4. If Black A, White B.

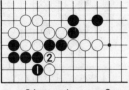

Wrong Answer 2

Black 1 loses two stones. Black has suffered a big loss.

PROBLEM 99

Correct Answer 1
Black 1 is the tesuji for linking up the black groups. If White 2, the sequence to Black 7 follows.

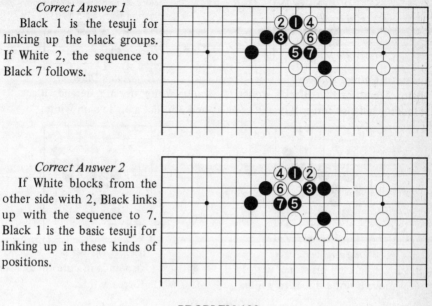

Correct Answer 2
If White blocks from the other side with 2, Black links up with the sequence to 7. Black 1 is the basic tesuji for linking up in these kinds of positions.

PROBLEM 100

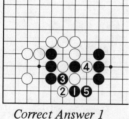

Correct Answer 1
Black 1 is the same kind of tesuji. Black links up with the sequence to 5.

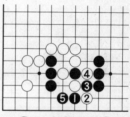

Correct Answer 2
If White blocks from the other side with 2, Black 3 and 5 safely link up.

Wrong Answer 1
Black 1 fails. The sequence to White 6 results in a ko.

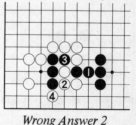

Wrong Answer 2
Black 1 is a terrible move. With the sequence to 4, Black loses four stones.

Correct Answer

Black 1 ensures that Black's stones will link up and also forces White 2.

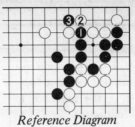

Reference Diagram

If White doesn't defend, Black 1 and 3 inflict a big loss on White.

Wrong Answer 1

Black can link up his stones with 1, but this move is not a threat to White.

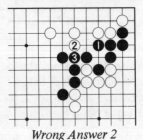

Wrong Answer 2

Black 1 also ends in gote for Black after White forces with 2.

PROBLEM 102

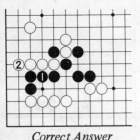

Correct Answer

Black 1 ensures that Black's stones will link up and also forces White 2.

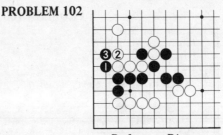

Reference Diagram

If White doesn't defend, Black 1 and 3 inflict a big loss on White.

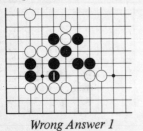

Wrong Answer 1

Black 1 doesn't threaten anything. White will play elsewhere.

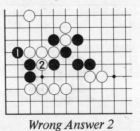

Wrong Answer 2

Black 1 is an overplay. Black is too thin to play so aggressively.

PROBLEM 103

Correct Answer

Black ataris with 1 and captures a stone with 3. If White 2 at **A**, Black ataris at 2 and the three white stones in the corner die.

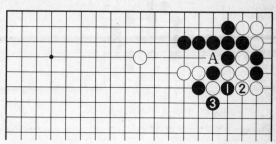

Wrong Answer

If Black connects at 1, White connects at 2. If Black 1 at **A**, White 2 and Black has failed.

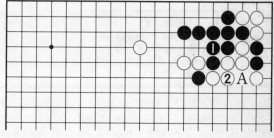

PROBLEM 104

Correct Answer

White should push through with 1. After 5, Black's shape is in tatters.

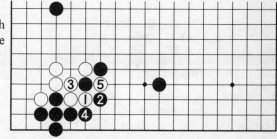

Wrong Answer

If White connects at 1, Black gets a strong position on the right when he plays at 2. White has failed.

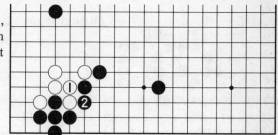

PROBLEM 105

Correct Answer

Wedging in with 1 enables Black to capture two stones with 3.

Wrong Answer

Directly giving atari with 1 fails. Black loses six stones after White 4.

PROBLEM 106

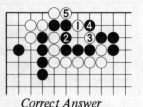

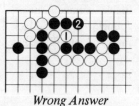

Correct Answer

White catches two black stones with 1. If Black 2, White 3 and 5.

Wrong Answer

White 1 is artless. Now the four white stones in the corner die.

PROBLEM 107

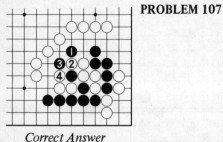

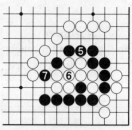

Correct Answer

Black 1 catches four white stones. It is futile to resist with White 2 and 4.

Continuation

Black gives atari with 5 and 7, killing nine white stones.

PROBLEM 108

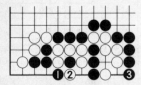

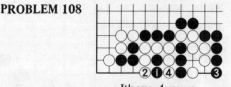

Correct Answer

Black 1 creates a shortage of liberties for White. After 3, the six white stones on the right die.

Wrong Answer

Black 1 fails. After Black 3, White 4 gives atari to three black stones.

PROBLEM 109

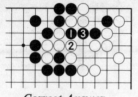

Correct Answer

If Black plays 1 and 3, he catches three white stones at the top.

Wrong Answer

Black 1 here is insufficient. Up to 4, Black has captured only one stone.

PROBLEM 110

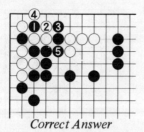

Correct Answer

Black cuts and sacrifices with 1 and 3. White's four stones on the right are separated from the corner after 5.

Wrong Answer

Black 1 lets White link up with 2. If 1 at 2, White 2 at 1.

PROBLEM 111

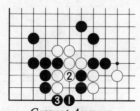

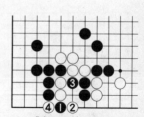

Correct Answer

Black can link up by playing 1 and 3. If White 2 at 3, Black 3 at 2.

Wrong Answer

Black 1 fails. White captures with 2 and 4. Black has no follow-up.

PROBLEM 112

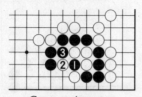

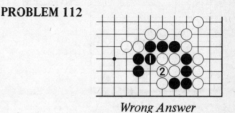

Correct Answer

Sacrificing a stone with 1 is the key move. White's five stones now die.

Wrong Answer

If Black 1, White connects at 2 and the four black stones to the right die.

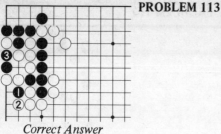

PROBLEM 113

Correct Answer

Black 1 sets up a shortage of liberties, so White can't save his four stones.

Wrong Answer

Without the cut, White can atari at 2 when Black captures at 1.

PROBLEM 114

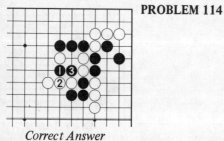

Correct Answer

By attaching at 1, Black can capture two white stones with 3.

Wrong Answer

If Black ataris with 1, White's stones escape when White connects at 2.

PROBLEM 115

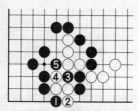

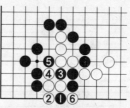

Correct Answer

By exchanging 1 for 2, Black captures the white stones on the left up to 5.

Wrong Answer

Black 1 here fails. Black loses four stones up to 6.

PROBLEM 116

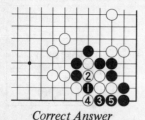

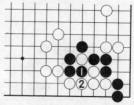

Correct Answer

Black sacrifices a stone with 1 and catches five white stones up to 5.

Wrong Answer

Black 1 captures only one stone. After 2, White's stones are safe.

PROBLEM 117

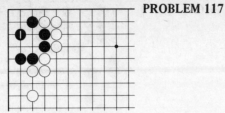

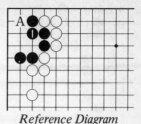

Correct Answer

Black 1 is the 'shape' move to live. You should remember this move.

Reference Diagram

Black at 1 or A also gets life for Black, but they are not as profitable.

PROBLEM 118

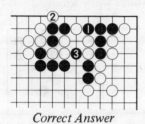

Correct Answer

Black 1 is the key point. With 3, Black captures two stones.

Wrong Answer

If Black 1 and 3, White 4 ataris Black first, so White can't be captured.

PROBLEM 119

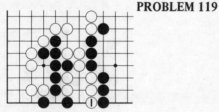

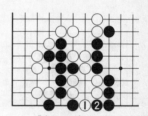

Correct Answer

White 1 separates Black, so his stones on the left will be captured.

Wrong Answer

If White ataris with 1, Black 2 makes the situation a ko.

PROBLEM 120

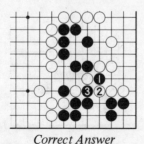

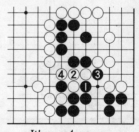

Correct Answer

If Black sacrifices a stones with 1, Black can link up his stones with 3.

Wrong Answer

Black 1 and 3 fail to link up, as can be seen after White plays 4.

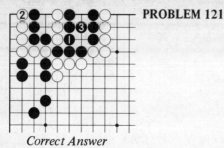

PROBLEM 121

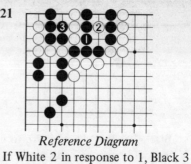

Correct Answer

Black 1 and 3 break the seki. All of White's stones on the left now die.

Reference Diagram

If White 2 in response to 1, Black 3 ataris three white stones.

PROBLEM 122

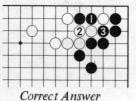

Correct Answer

Black 1 is the vital point. After White 2, Black captures a stone with 3.

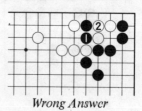

Wrong Answer

If Black 1, White 2 catches the two black stones on the left.

PROBLEM 123

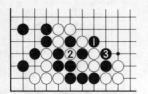

Correct Answer

Black 1 is the vital point to break out of confinement. After Black 3 —

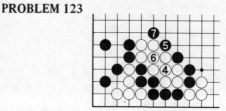

Continuation

If White 4 and 6, Black catches White in a ladder with 7.

PROBLEM 124

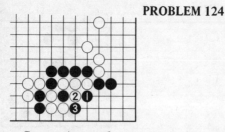

Correct Answer 1

Black 1 captures three white stones.

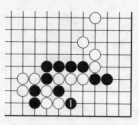

Correct Answer 2

Black 1 also catches three white stones.

PROBLEM 125

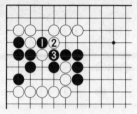

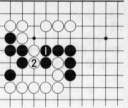

Correct Answer

Black cuts at 1. After White 2, Black 3 ensures the linkup.

Wrong Answer

If Black 1, White 2 separates Black into two groups.

PROBLEM 126

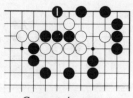

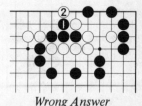

Correct Answer

If Black jumps to 1, there is no way White can stop Black from linking up.

Wrong Answer

If Black 1, White 2 will capture four black stones.

PROBLEM 127

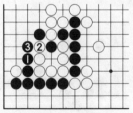

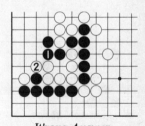

Correct Answer

Black 1 and 3 capture seven white stones in a snapback.

Wrong Answer

If Black 1, White increases his liberties and Black's stones on the right die.

PROBLEM 128

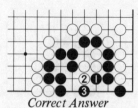

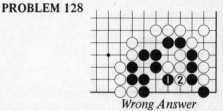

Correct Answer

Black 1 and 3 capture four white stones.

Wrong Answer

If Black 1, White 2 ataris three black stones. Black has failed.

PROBLEM 129

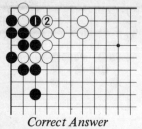

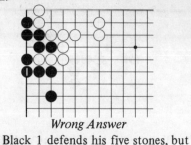

Correct Answer

Black can defend his five stones and keep sente by playing at 1.

Wrong Answer

Black 1 defends his five stones, but now it is White who has sente.

PROBLEM 130

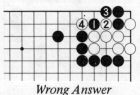

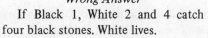

Correct Answer

Black 1 links up his two stones in the corner and kills the white stones.

Wrong Answer

If Black 1, White 2 and 4 catch four black stones. White lives.

PROBLEM 131

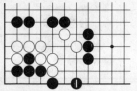

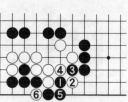

Correct Answer

Black links up his stones to the ones on the outside with 1.

Wrong Answer

Black 1 fails to link up, as the sequence to White 6 demonstrates.

PROBLEM 132

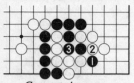

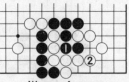

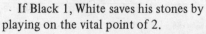

Correct Answer

Black 1 is the vital point for capturing the six white stones.

Wrong Answer

If Black 1, White saves his stones by playing on the vital point of 2.

PROBLEM 133

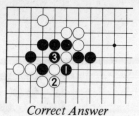

Correct Answer

Black 1 and 3 capture a white stone. If White 2 at 3, Black 3 at 2.

Wrong Answer

If Black 1, Black's stones in the corner are in grave danger after White 2.

PROBLEM 134

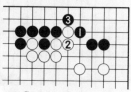

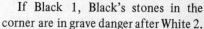
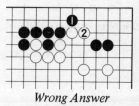

Correct Answer

Black 1 and 3 enable him to link up his two groups of stones.

Wrong Answer

When Black plays 1, he suffers major damage when White plays 2.

PROBLEM 135

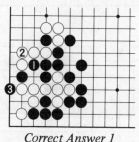

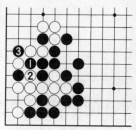

Correct Answer 1

Black 1 and 3 catch the nine white stones in the corner.

Correct Answer 2

If White 2 here, Black double ataris with 3.

PROBLEM 136

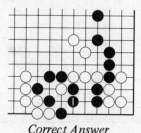

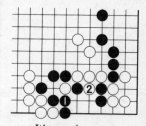

Correct Answer

Black catches a stone and makes two eyes for his group by playing 1.

Wrong Answer

If Black 1, White captures two black stones with 2. Black has failed.

PROBLEM 137

Correct Answer

Pressing down on the lone black stone with 1 is the most important point to play in this position. This move prevents Black from expanding his position at the top. If White were to play any other point, Black would play at A, building a large framework of territory at the top.

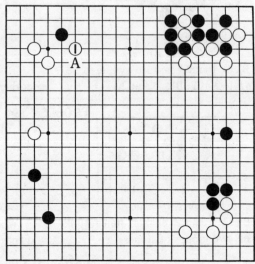

Reference Diagram

White 1 is unsatisfactory in the face of Black 2. The same can be said of White 1 at C. Both of these moves are inferior to White 1 in the Correct Answer.

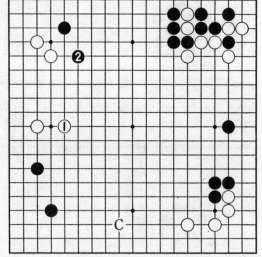

PROBLEM 138

Correct Answer

Of the three points in the problem diagram, Black 1 is the best. It not only attacks the two white stones but also extends from the black position at the top.

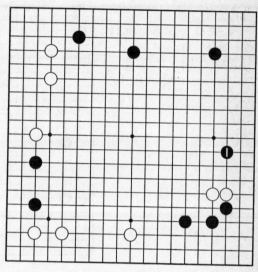

Reference Diagram

Black A would be unsatisfactory. It tightly reinforces Black's position at the top right, but it puts no pressure on the two white stones at the bottom.

Black C is also a good point, but in this position the right side is the most important.

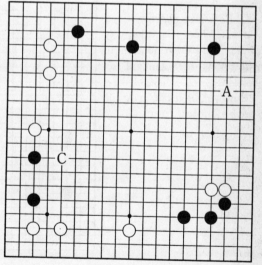

Correct Answer

Black 1, followed by 3, is the standard response. Black's stones end with good shape.

Before playing 3, Black could first exchange A for B.

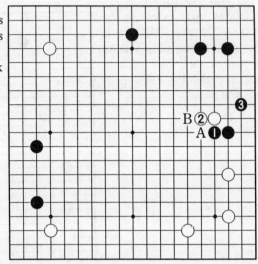

Reference Diagram

Black 1 here is another way to play. The continuation to White 6 is the standard sequence.

However, Black 1 at A and 5 are bad moves.

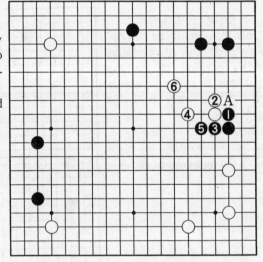

PROBLEM 140

Correct Answer
Black 1 is the standard way to play in this position.

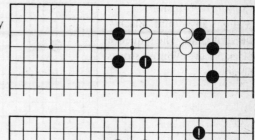

Reference Diagram
Depending on the circumstances, Black 1 or Black A could be played. You can't say that these moves are bad.

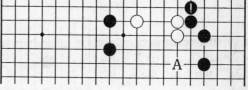

PROBLEM 141

Correct Answer
Black 1 and 3 are the best moves in this position. After 4, White's position on the left is too low, while Black's extension from his wall is ideal.

Wrong Answer
Black 1 is in the wrong direction. White 2 works very well in conjunction with his stone to the left of the side star-point.

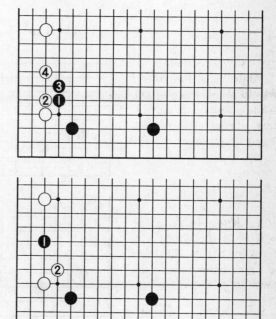

PROBLEM 142

Correct Answer
Without any doubt, Black 1 is the vital point. The sequence to Black 5 leaves White's stones vulnerable.

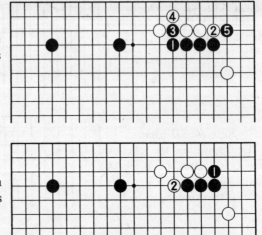

Wrong Answer
If Black 1, 2 gives White a strong position. Black has failed.

PROBLEM 143

Correct Answer
White 1 is the correct way to play in this position. White's position at the bottom is now perfectly balanced.

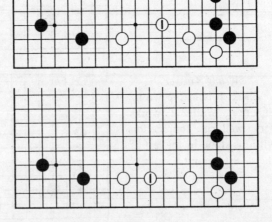

Wrong Answer
This is the wrong way for White to play. His stones at the bottom are too low.

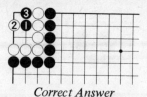

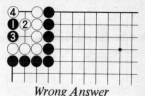

Correct Answer

Because of shortage of liberties, Black 1 and 3 kill White.

Wrong Answer

Black 1 and 3 here fail. After White 4, White can get a ko.

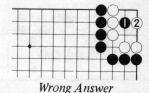

Correct Answer

Black gets a ko up to 5. Black 3 at A is also a ko, but 3 in the diagram is more profitable.

Wrong Answer

Black 1 fails. After 2, White has enough liberties to live.

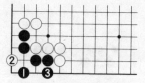

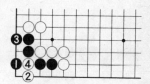

Correct Answer

Black 1 is the vital point for making two eyes. If White 2, Black lives with 3.

Wrong Answer

If Black 1, Black can't attack White after 4 because of shortage of liberties.

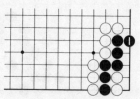

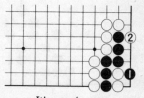

Correct Answer

Black 1 is the vital point. There is now nothing White can do to kill Black.

Wrong Answer

If Black 1, Black dies because of a shortage of liberties after White 2.

PROBLEM 148

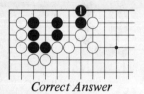

Correct Answer

After Black 1, Black can live no matter how White plays.

Wrong Answer

If Black 1, White 2 and 4 kill Black.

PROBLEM 149

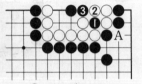

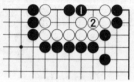

Correct Answer

Black 1 and 3 kill White. Finally, if White 4 at 1, Black defends at A.

Wrong Answer

Black 1 allows White to live with a seki after 2.

PROBLEM 150

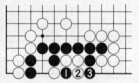

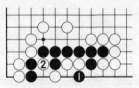

Correct Answer

Black sacrifices with 1. After 3, Black captures three stones and lives.

Wrong Answer

If 1 here, Black dies after White 2. Even if Black plays 1 at 2, he still dies.

PROBLEM 151

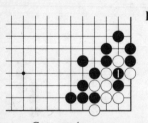

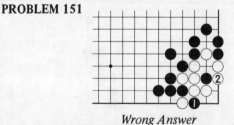

Correct Answer

If Black sacrifices two stones with 1, White will die.

Wrong Answer

Black 1 here fails. White 2 gives White two eyes.

PROBLEM 152

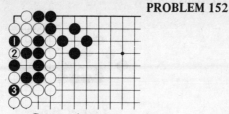

Correct Answer

Black 1 creates a double ko. The four corner white stones will now die.

Continuation

If White plays 1 after making a ko threat, Black takes the other ko with 2.

PROBLEM 153

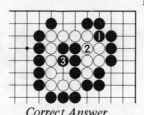

Correct Answer

Black ataris with 1 and then makes a 5-space big eye with 3. White is dead.

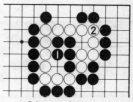

Wrong Answer

Trying to make a big eye first with 1 fails. After 2, the eye is too big.

PROBLEM 154

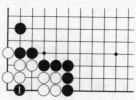

Correct Answer

Black 1 is the right point to attack. White is dead.

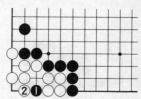

Wrong Answer

If Black captures four stones after 2, White can live by capturing two stones with the 'under-the-stones' tesuji.

PROBLEM 155

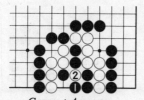

Correct Answer

Black 1 is the vital point to make a big eye. If White captures with 2 —

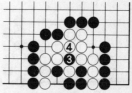

Continuation

After the exchange of 3 for 4, White has a dead 6-space big eye shape.

PROBLEM 156

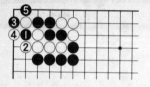

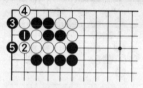

Correct Answer 1

Black can get a ko with the sequence up to 5.

Correct Answer 2

If White plays 4 as here, it is still a ko after Black 5.

PROBLEM 157

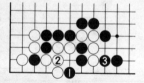

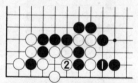

Correct Answer

If Black 1, followed by 3, Black wins the capturing race by one move.

Wrong Answer

Playing Black 1 first is wrong. Black loses the capturing race.

PROBLEM 158

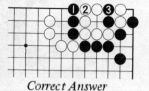

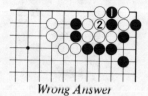

Correct Answer

Threatening a snapback with 1, followed by 3, wins the capturing race.

Wrong Answer

Black 1 here fails. White catches two stones when he plays 2.

PROBLEM 159

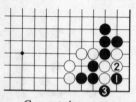

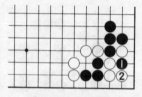

Correct Answer

Black 1 is the vital point here. After 3 Black catches four white stones.

Wrong Answer

Black 1 catches a stone, but after 2 Black loses three stones at the bottom.

PROBLEM 160

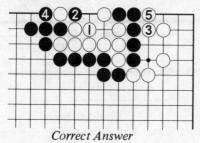

Correct Answer

White increases his liberties by one move if he plays 1. The five stones on the right can now be captured.

Wrong Answer

Going after the five black stones with 1 results in a ko up to 4. If 1 at A, Black plays at 3 and White loses.

PROBLEM 161

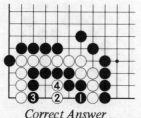

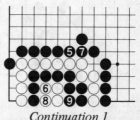

Correct Answer

Black 1 and 3 make a big eye. After White 4 —

Continuation 1

Black starts filling in the liberties on the outside. After taking with 9 —

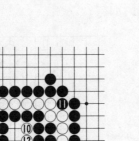

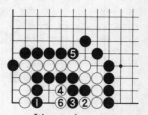

Continuation 2

From here you can see that Black wins the capturing race by one move.

Wrong Answer

White 2 is the vital point. If Black plays 1, Black loses the capturing race.

PROBLEM 162

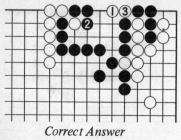

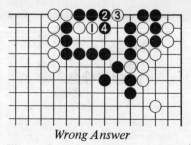

Correct Answer

White 1 is the vital point. If Black 2, White catches four stones with 3. If Black 2 at 3, White catches two stones on the left by playing at 2.

Wrong Answer

The order of moves is important. If White 1 first, White has no follow-up after Black 4.

PROBLEM 163

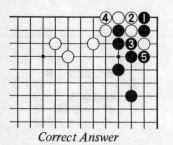

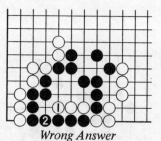

Correct Answer

White should sacrifice a stone with 1. If Black 2, White 3 catches three black stones.

Wrong Answer

White can't catch anything with 1. Black defends at 2 and he has no shortage of liberties.

PROBLEM 164

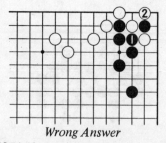

Correct Answer

Black 1 is the key point. Up to 5, Black unconditionally captures a white stone.

Wrong Answer

If Black 1, a ko arises in the corner. This is a failure for Black.

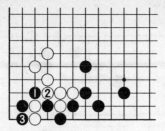

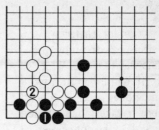

Correct Answer

Black 1 and 3 catch two white stones by setting up a snapback. You have to watch out for moves like 3.

Wrong Answer

If Black 1, Black suffers a big loss after White 2.

PROBLEM 166

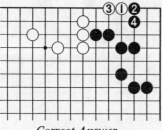

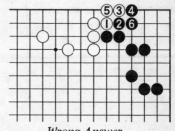

Correct Answer

The 'monkey jump' of White 1 is the best way to eat into Black's territory. Black 2 is the best answer here, but in other situations different replies are necessary.

Wrong Answer

These moves are inferior to the correct answer.

PROBLEM 167

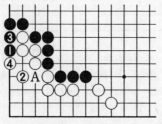

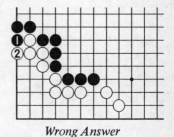

Correct Answer

Black 1 is the best move. White must respond submissively with 2 and 4. White 2 at 3 is unreasonable because of Black A.

Wrong Answer

Compared to the correct answer, Black 1 is two points inferior.

Correct Answer

Black 1 is the most profitable way to reduce White's area. If White captures two black stones after 3, Black simply retakes one stone to maintain the connection.

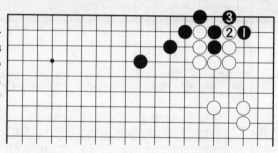

Wrong Answer

Black 1 is inferior. White blocks with 2. Compared to the correct answer, this diagram is much less profitable.

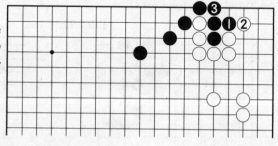

PROBLEM 169

Correct Answer

Black 1 is the most profitable way to catch the lone white stone on the left. White 2 at 3 would be unreasonable. In that case, Black would atari at 2.

Wrong Answer

The sequence to 3 is greatly inferior to the correct answer.

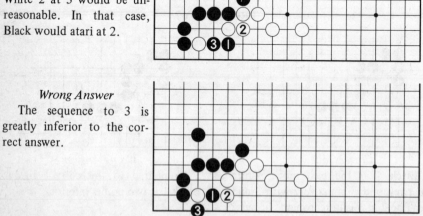

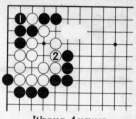

PROBLEM 170

Correct Answer

Black 1 is the vital point. White is dead after Black plays 3.

Wrong Answer

If Black 1, White lives by playing 2. If Black 1 at 2, White 2 at 1.

PROBLEM 171

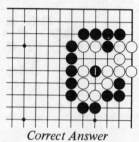

Correct Answer

If Black plays 1, White's second eye is false no matter what he does.

Wrong Answer

Black 1 will capture two stones, but the main body of White's group lives.

PROBLEM 172

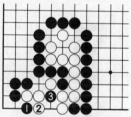
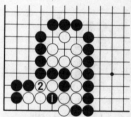

Correct Answer

Black 1 and 3 are the correct order. White's second eye at the edge is false.

Wrong Answer

If Black 1, White lives with 2. If Black 1 at 2, White lives with 2 at 1.

PROBLEM 173

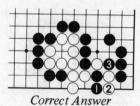
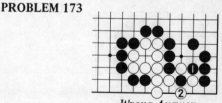

Correct Answer

Black 1 and 3 kill White. If White takes two stones, Black plays above 1.

Wrong Answer

Black 1 fails. White is alive after he captures with 2.

PROBLEM 174

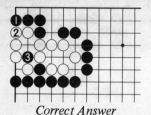

Correct Answer

Black 1 is the vital point. If White 2, then Black kills White with 3.

Wrong Answer

If Black 1, White lives by playing 2.

PROBLEM 175

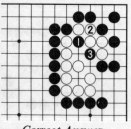

Correct Answer

Black 1 is the vital point. If White 2, White dies when Black plays 3.

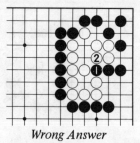

Wrong Answer

If Black 1, White gets two eyes when he plays at 2.

PROBLEM 176

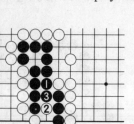

Correct Answer

Black 1 is the vital point. If White ataris with 2, Black lives with 3.

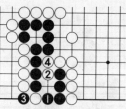

Wrong Answer

If Black 1, White 2 and 4 kill Black.

PROBLEM 177

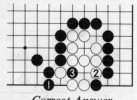

Correct Answer

Black 1 is the vital point. If White 2, Black 3 kills White.

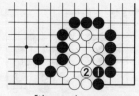

Wrong Answer

If Black 1, White gets two eyes and lives when he plays 2.

PROBLEM 178

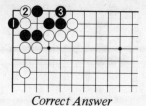

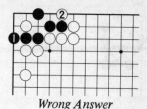

Correct Answer

Black 1 is the vital point. If White 2, Black lives with 3.

Wrong Answer

If Black plays 1, he can't get two eyes after White 2.

PROBLEM 179

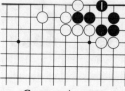

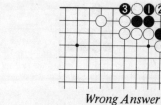

Correct Answer

Black gets two eyes and lives when he plays 1.

Wrong Answer

If Black plays at 1, he can't get two eyes after White 2 and 4.

PROBLEM 180

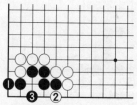

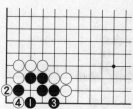

Correct Answer

Black 1 is the vital point. If White 2, Black lives with 3.

Wrong Answer

If Black 1, Black's group can live only if he wins the ko after 2 and 4.

PROBLEM 181

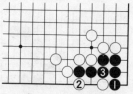

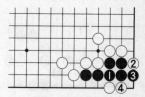

Correct Answer

Black gets two eyes and lives when he plays 1 and 3.

Wrong Answer

Black fails if he plays 1. He can't get two eyes after White 2 and 4.

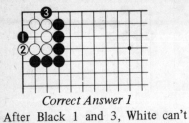

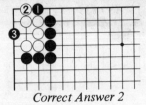

Correct Answer 1

After Black 1 and 3, White can't get two eyes, so he dies.

Correct Answer 2

Playing 1 and 3 in this order also kills White.

PROBLEM 183

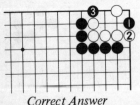

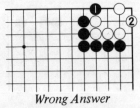

Correct Answer

Black 1 is the vital point. After Black 3, White is dead.

Wrong Answer

If Black 1, White gets two eyes and lives when he plays 2.

PROBLEM 184

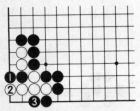

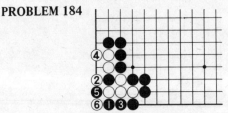

Correct Answer

Black 1 and 3 prevent White from getting two eyes, so White is dead.

Wrong Answer

If Black 1, the sequence to 6 results in a ko. Black has failed.

PROBLEM 185

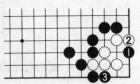

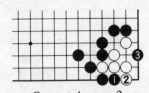

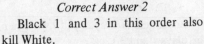

Correct Answer 1

If Black 1 and 3, White can't get two eyes, so he dies.

Correct Answer 2

Black 1 and 3 in this order also kill White.

PROBLEM 186

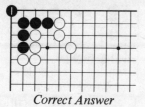

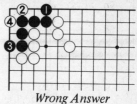

Correct Answer

Black 1 ensures that Black will get two eyes and life.

Wrong Answer

It may look like a seki after Black 1 and 3, but it is not. Black is dead.

PROBLEM 187

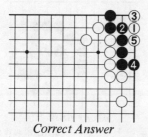

Correct Answer

The sequence up to 5 gives Black the dead-bent-four-in-the-corner shape.

Wrong Answer

If White 1, Black plays on the vital point of 2 and lives up to 4.

PROBLEM 188

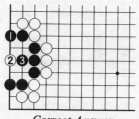

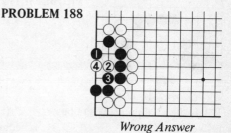

Correct Answer

Black 1 makes the 'comb' formation. If White 2, Black lives with 3.

Wrong Answer

If Black 1, he dies after the sequence to White 4.

PROBLEM 189

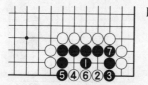

Correct Answer

Black 1 is the vital point. The sequence to Black 7 results in a seki.

Wrong Answer

If Black 1, the sequence to White 6 kills Black.

PROBLEM 190

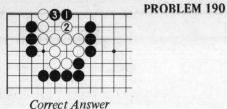

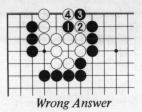

Correct Answer

After 3, Black will sacrifice two stones, leaving White with a dead shape.

Wrong Answer

If 1 and 3, White sacrifices 4, but he can then recapture 1 and live.

PROBLEM 191

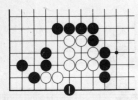

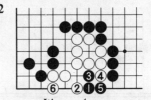

Correct Answer

After 1, White dies since he can't avoid the capture of two of his stones.

Wrong Answer

Black 1 doesn't capture anything. White lives by playing 2.

PROBLEM 192

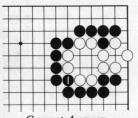

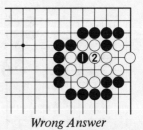

Correct Answer

Black 1 is the vital point. White has only one eye, so he dies.

Wrong Answer

If Black 1, White lives with the sequence to 6.

PROBLEM 193

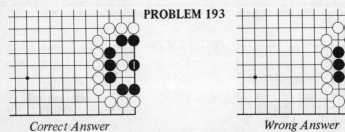

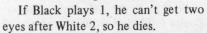

Correct Answer

If Black plays the vital point of 1, he lives.

Wrong Answer

If Black plays 1, he can't get two eyes after White 2, so he dies.

PROBLEM 194

Correct Answer

White 1 is the vital point. After 3, Black is left with a dead 3-space big eye.

Wrong Answer

If White 1, Black can live after he captures three stones with 4.

PROBLEM 195

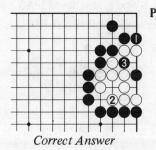

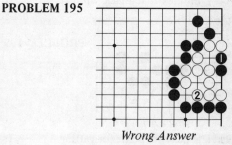

Correct Answer

Black 1 sets up a snapback. If White defends at 3 with 2, Black plays 3 at 2.

Wrong Answer

Black 1 fails. White 2 makes two eyes. If Black 1 at 2, White 2 at 1.

PROBLEM 196

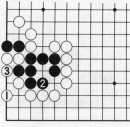

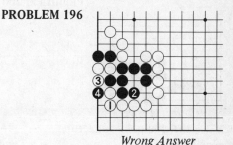

Correct Answer

After 1, White sacrifices three stones with 3. If Black captures, White retakes at 3, leaving Black with a false eye.

Wrong Answer

White 1 here doesn't permit the three-stone sacrifice as in the correct answer. After 4, Black is alive.

PROBLEM 197

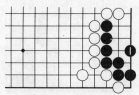

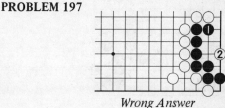

Correct Answer

Black 1 is the vital point for making two eyes.

Wrong Answer

If Black 1, White strikes at the vital point with 2, killing Black.

PROBLEM 198

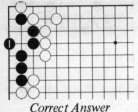

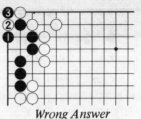

Correct Answer

Black 1 ensures that Black will get two eyes and life.

Wrong Answer

If Black 1, the life of Black's group depends on the result of a ko.

PROBLEM 199

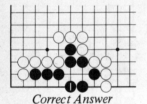

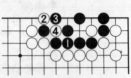

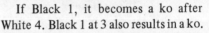

Correct Answer

Black 1 is the vital point for getting two eyes and life.

Wrong Answer

If Black 1, it becomes a ko after White 4. Black 1 at 3 also results in a ko.

PROBLEM 200

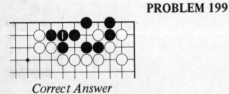

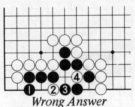

Correct Answer

Black 1 is the vital point for getting two eyes and life.

Wrong Answer

If Black 1, the combination of White 2 and 4 kills Black.

PROBLEM 201

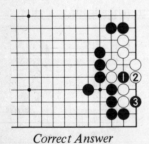

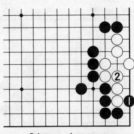

Correct Answer

After Black 1 and 3, the white group dies.

Wrong Answer

If Black 1, White plays 2, getting two eyes and life.

PROBLEM 202

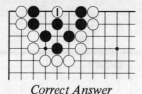

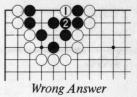

Correct Answer
White 1 sets up a snapback on either side, so Black dies.

Wrong Answer
If White ataris with 1, Black defends with 2 and lives.

PROBLEM 203

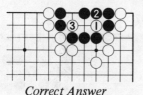

Correct Answer
White 1 and 3 kill the black group. White 1 at 3 first also kills Black.

Wrong Answer
White 1 fails. Black lives by playing at 2.

PROBLEM 204

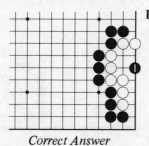

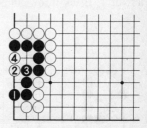

Correct Answer
Black 1 is the vital point for making two eyes.

Wrong Answer
If Black 1, White 2 and 4 give the black group a dead 3-space big eye.

PROBLEM 205

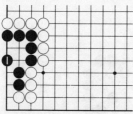

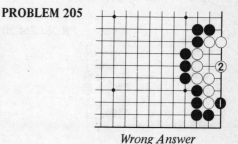

Correct Answer
After Black 1, there is no way that White can make two eyes.

Wrong Answer
If Black 1, White gets two eyes and lives by playing at 2.

PROBLEM 206

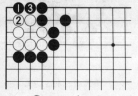

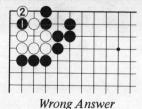

Correct Answer

Black 1 is the vital point. If White 2, Black 3 and White dies.

Wrong Answer

If Black plays 1, White 2 gives White two eyes and life.

PROBLEM 207

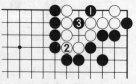

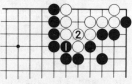

Correct Answer

Black 1 and 3 kill White. If 2 is to the left of 1, Black throws in below 3.

Wrong Answer

If Black exchanges 1 for 2, White gets a living 4-space big eye.

PROBLEM 208

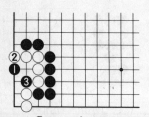

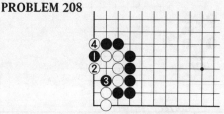

Correct Answer

Black 1 is the vital point. If White 2, White has no follow-up after Black 3.

Wrong Answer

Black 1 and 3 fail. After White captures with 4, White can't be killed.

PROBLEM 209

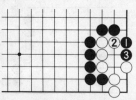

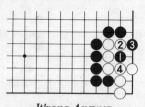

Correct Answer

Black 1 and 3 prevent White from getting two eyes and life.

Wrong Answer

If Black 1, White lives with the sequence up to 4.

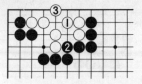 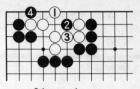

Correct Answer
White 1 is the vital point. White can live with the sequence to 3.

Wrong Answer
If White 1, Black 2 and 4 prevent White from getting two eyes.

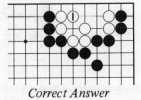 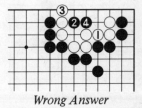

Correct Answer
If White plays 1, there is no way that Black can kill White.

Wrong Answer
If White 1, White will be reduced to a dead 3-space big eye after 2 and 4.

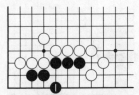 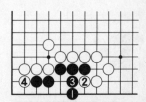

Correct Answer
Black 1 is the vital point for getting two eyes and life.

Wrong Answer
If Black 1, Black dies after White 2 and 4. If Black 1 at 3, White 2 at 4.

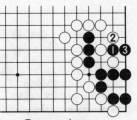 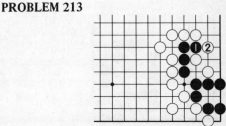

Correct Answer
Black 1 and 3 capture one white stone and give Black life.

Wrong Answer
If Black exchanges 1 for 2, there is no way that he can live.

PROBLEM 214

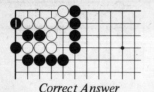

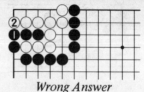

Correct Answer

Black 1 kills White. If White takes two stones, Black retakes a stone.

Wrong Answer

If Black plays 1, White gets a living shape in the corner with 2.

PROBLEM 215

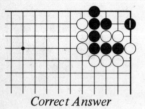

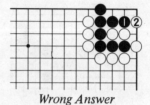

Correct Answer

If Black plays 1, he will get two eyes and his stones will live.

Wrong Answer

If Black plays 1, his stones are dead after White 2.

PROBLEM 216

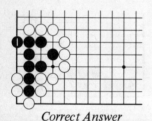

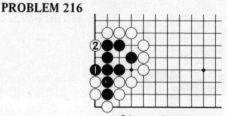

Correct Answer

If Black plays 1, White can't prevent Black from getting two eyes.

Wrong Answer

If Black 1, White 2 gives up two stones but destroys Black's second eye.

PROBLEM 217

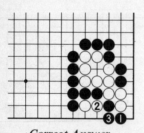

Correct Answer

Black 1 is the vital point. After Black 3, White is dead.

Wrong Answer

Black 1 lets White get a second eye and life with 2.

PROBLEM 218

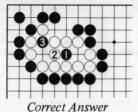

Correct Answer

Black 1 and 3 prevent White from getting two eyes, so White dies.

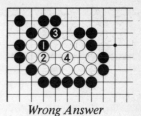

Wrong Answer

Black 1 fails. White lives with 2 and 4.

PROBLEM 219

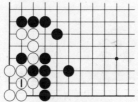

Correct Answer

Black kills White by sacrificing three stones with the sequence up to 5.

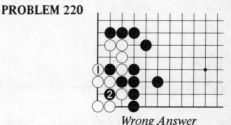

Wrong Answer

If Black 1, White lives by playing 2 and 4.

PROBLEM 220

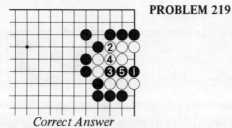

Correct Answer

White 1 ensures that White will get two eyes and life.

Wrong Answer

If White 1, Black kills White by destroying his eye in the corner with 2.

PROBLEM 221

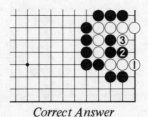

Correct Answer

White 1 and 3 are the vital points for White to live.

Wrong Answer

If White plays 1 first, Black 2 and 4 give White a dead 3-space big eye.

PROBLEM 222

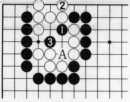

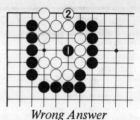

Correct Answer

Black 1 and 3 kill White by threatening a snapback at A.

Wrong Answer

If Black 1, White can live by playing 2. If Black 1 at 2, White 2 at 1.

PROBLEM 223

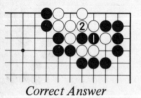

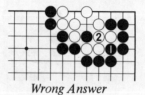

Correct Answer

Black kills White by sacrificing two stones with 1 and then playing 3 at 1.

Wrong Answer

If Black 1, White gets two eyes and lives with 2.

PROBLEM 224

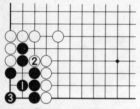

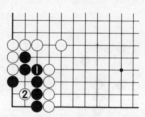

Correct Answer

Black 1 is the vital point. If White 2, Black lives with 3.

Wrong Answer

If Black plays 1, he is reduced to a 5-space big eye, so he dies.

PROBLEM 225

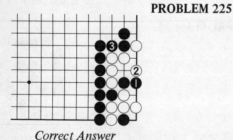

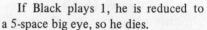

Correct Answer

If Black plays 1 and 3, White dies because of shortage of liberties.

Wrong Answer

White answers 1 with 2 and 4. White now captures three stones, so he lives.

PROBLEM 226

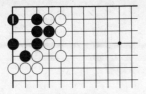

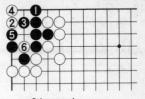

Correct Answer

Black 1 is the vital point for ensuring that the black stones will live.

Wrong Answer

In answer to Black 1, White strikes at the vital point of 2, killing Black.

PROBLEM 227

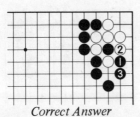

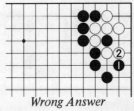

Correct Answer

If Black plays 1 and 3, White can't get two eyes, so his stones die.

Wrong Answer

If Black plays 1, White gets two eyes and life with 2.

PROBLEM 228

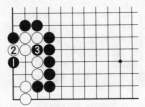

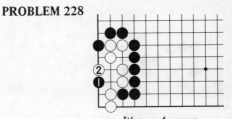

Correct Answer

Black 1 and 3 (or 3 to the right of 1) kill White.

Wrong Answer

If Black plays 1, White can live by playing at 2.

PROBLEM 229

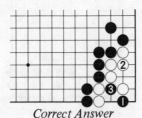

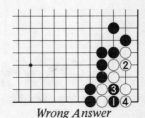

Correct Answer

Black 1 sets up a snapback at 3. If 2 at 3, Black 3 at 2 also kills White.

Wrong Answer

If Black 1, White can live by giving up two stones with 2 and 4.

PROBLEM 230

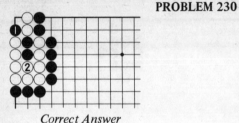

Correct Answer

Black 1 is the vital point. White captures two stones with 2, but —

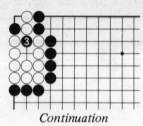

Continuation

Black sets up a snapback with 3. The white stones are now dead.

PROBLEM 231

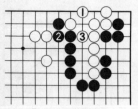

Correct Answer

White lives if he plays 1. If Black 2 at 3, White 3 at 2.

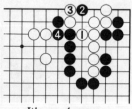

Wrong Answer

In response to 1, Black plays 2 and 4, killing White.

PROBLEM 232

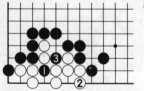

Correct Answer

Even if White plays 2, 1 and 3 make White's second eye false, so he dies.

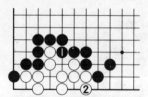

Wrong Answer

In answer to Black 1, White can get two eyes and live with 2.

PROBLEM 233

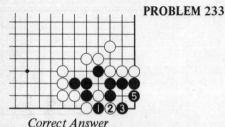

Correct Answer

Black sacrifices a stone with 1 and lives with 3 and 5. (White 4 at Black 1.)

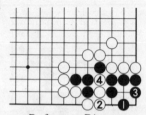

Reference Diagram

Black can live with 1 and 3, but he loses four stones when White plays 4.

PROBLEM 234

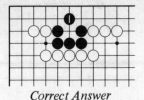

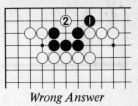

Correct Answer

If Black plays on the central point with 1, he can make another eye either to the left or to the right.

Wrong Answer

If Black plays on any other point, White will kill Black by striking at the vital point of 2.

PROBLEM 235

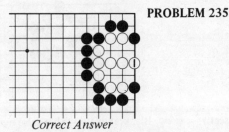

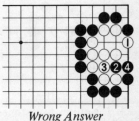

Correct Answer

The central point is crucial. White can now get two eyes above and below.

Wrong Answer

If White 1, White is left with only one eye after Black 2 and 4.

PROBLEM 236

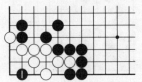

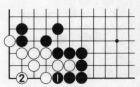

Correct Answer

Black 1 is the vital point for killing White.

Wrong Answer

If Black 1, White sacrifices two stones and lives with 2.

PROBLEM 237

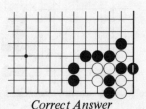

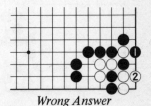

Correct Answer

If Black plays 1, White can get only one eye in the corner, so White dies.

Wrong Answer

If Black captures a stone with 1, White gets his second eye at 2.

PROBLEM 238

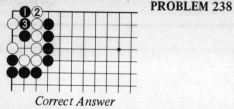

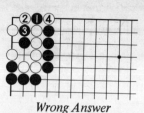

Correct Answer

Black kills White with the sequence to 3.

Wrong Answer

Black 1 is answered by White 2 and 4. White easily lives.

PROBLEM 239

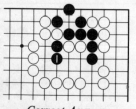

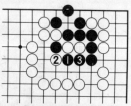

Correct Answer

Black 1 captures two stones, securing the eye he needs to live.

Wrong Answer

Black ends up with a false eye when White plays 4 above Black 1.

PROBLEM 240

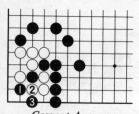

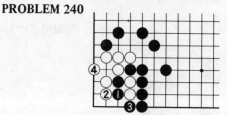

Correct Answer

Black 1 and 3 leave White with only one eye, so he is dead.

Wrong Answer

Black 1 and 3 cleanly capture two white stones, but White lives with 4.

PROBLEM 241

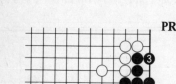

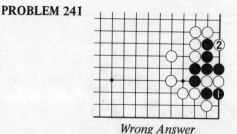

Correct Answer

Black sets up a snapback with 1 and then makes his second eye at 3.

Wrong Answer

If Black captures two stones with 1, White destroys the second eye with 2.

PROBLEM 242

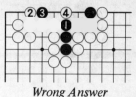

Correct Answer

Black 1 is the vital point. If White takes two stones, Black retakes one.

Wrong Answer

If Black plays 1, he ends up with a dead 3-space big eye after 2 and 4.

PROBLEM 243

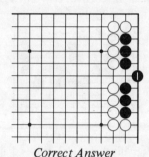

Correct Answer

Black lives with 1. He can now get an eye both above and below.

Wrong Answer

The proverb 'eight live, six die' is well illustrated by this sequence.

PROBLEM 244

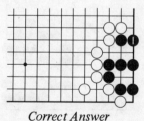

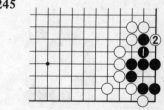

Correct Answer

Black 1 and 3 reduce White to a dead 3-space big eye.

Wrong Answer

Black 1 allows White to play on the vital point for getting two eyes.

PROBLEM 245

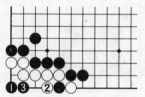

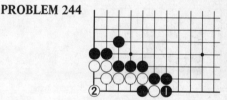

Correct Answer

Black 1 ensures that Black will get two eyes and life.

Wrong Answer

If Black 1, White destroys Black's second eye with 2.

PROBLEM 246

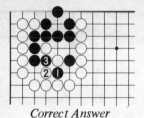

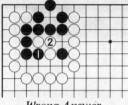

Correct Answer

Black can get two eyes and life by playing 1 and 3.

Wrong Answer

In answer to 1, White connects at 2 and Black is left with only one eye.

PROBLEM 247

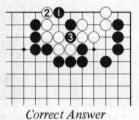

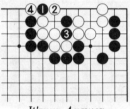

Correct Answer

Black 1 and 3 kill all the white stones.

Wrong Answer

After Black 1 and 3 in this diagram, White lives by capturing with 2 and 4.

PROBLEM 248

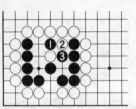

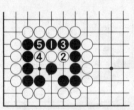

Correct Answer

Black 1 is the central point of a symmetrical shape. Black 3 gets two eyes.

Reference Diagram

In the worst case, Black lives in a seki, as the sequence to 5 shows.

PROBLEM 249

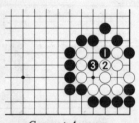

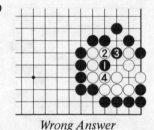

Correct Answer

Black 1 and 3 destroy White's eyes, killing the white stones.

Wrong Answer

Black 1 fails. White lives by capturing a stone for his second eye.

PROBLEM 250

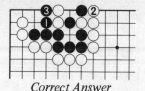

Correct Answer

Black 1 and 3 sacrifice a stone, but then Black retakes three stones and gets two eyes.

Wrong Answer

In response to 1, White ataris at 2, killing the black stones.

PROBLEM 251

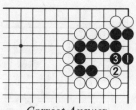

Correct Answer

Black can get two eyes and life by playing 1 and 3.

Wrong Answer

If Black 1, the only way Black can live is to win a ko.

PROBLEM 252

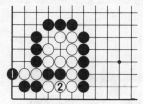

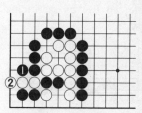

Correct Answer

Black kills White by playing at 1, then throwing in a stone two spaces to the right of 1.

Wrong Answer

If Black exchanges 1 for 2, White will live by capturing the two stones in the corner.

PROBLEM 253

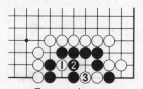

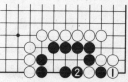

Correct Answer

White kills Black by destroying one of his two eyes with 1 and 3.

Wrong Answer

If White 1, Black makes a living 4-space big eye with 2.

PROBLEM 254

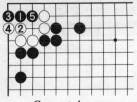

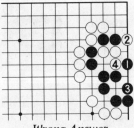

Correct Answer

Black 1 is the vital point of the 'carpenter's square'. Up to 5, White is left with a dead 3-space big eye.

Reference Diagram

Black 1, as well as Black 1 at 4, also kills White, but the standard attacking move is Black 1 in the correct answer.

PROBLEM 255

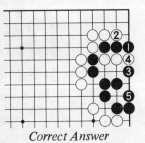

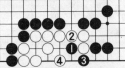

Correct Answer

Black can live by sacrificing three stones with 1.

Wrong Answer

Against Black 1, White kills Black with 2 and 4.

PROBLEM 256

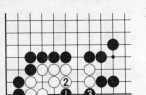

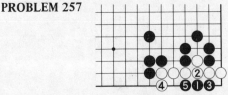

Correct Answer

Black 1 is the vital point. White dies after the sequence to 3.

Wrong Answer

Black 1 fails to kill White. White lives with 2 and 4.

PROBLEM 257

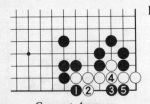

Correct Answer

Black attacks with 1 and 3. After Black 5, White is dead.

Wrong Answer

Black 1 is the wrong order. White lives with a seki.

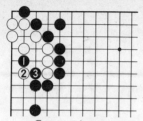

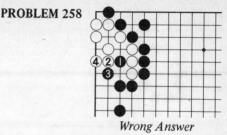

PROBLEM 258

Correct Answer

Black 1 kills White by taking advantage of his shortage of liberties.

Wrong Answer

If Black plays 1, White lives with 2 and 4.

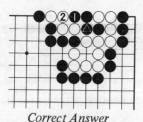

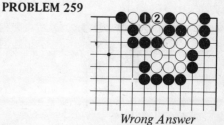

PROBLEM 259

Correct Answer

Black 1 sets up the 'under the stones' tesuji. Black 3 at ▲ captures White.

Wrong Answer

If Black 1, Black has no follow-up after White captures with 2.

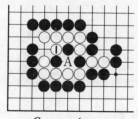

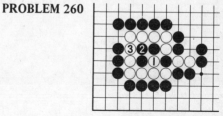

PROBLEM 260

Correct Answer

After White 1, connecting at A would be suicide, so White lives.

Wrong Answer

If White captures with 1 and 3, he dies after Black plays back in with 4 at 2.

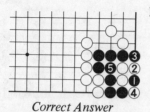

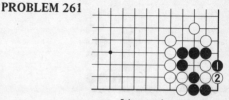

PROBLEM 261

Correct Answer

After the sequence to 5, White can't connect at 1, so Black lives.

Wrong Answer

If Black 1, Black ends up with a dead 3-space big eye after White 2.

PROBLEM 262

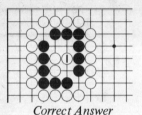

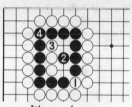

Correct Answer

White 1 is the vital point for giving Black a dead 5-space big eye.

Wrong Answer

If White 1, Black gets a seki with 2 and 4.

PROBLEM 263

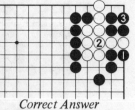

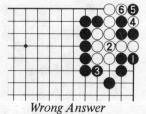

Correct Answer

Black gives White a dead 4-space big eye by playing 1 and 3.

Wrong Answer

If Black 3, White lives with 4 and 6, since connecting at 4 is suicide for Black.

PROBLEM 264

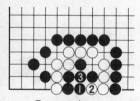

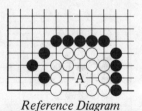

Correct Answer

If Black plays 1 and 3, White is left with a dead 6-space big eye.

Reference Diagram

This shape is known as 'flowery six'. If Black plays at A, White is dead.

PROBLEM 265

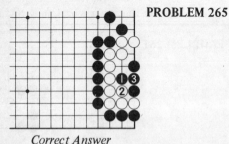

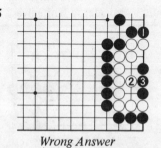

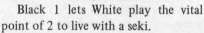

Correct Answer

Black 1 and 3 make a 5-space big eye. White dies.

Wrong Answer

Black 1 lets White play the vital point of 2 to live with a seki.

PROBLEM 266

 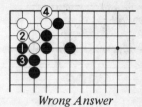

Correct Answer

Black 1 and 3 result in a ko. If White 2 at 3, Black A kills White outright.

Wrong Answer

If Black 1 and 3, White lives unconditionally with 2 and 4.

PROBLEM 267

Correct Answer

The sequence to White 4 results in a ko. White 2 at 4 also results in a ko, but this ko would be worse for White.

Wrong Answer

If Black 1, there is no ko. White is unconditionally alive after 2.

PROBLEM 268

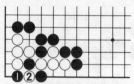 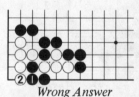

Correct Answer

Black 1 sets up a ko for the white group.

Wrong Answer

If Black 1, White catches three black stones and lives with 2.

PROBLEM 269

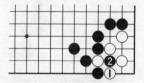 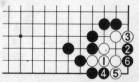

Correct Answer

The only way White can save his stones is to start a ko with 1.

Wrong Answer

If White 1, White is reduced to a dead 3-space big eye up to Black 6.

PROBLEM 270

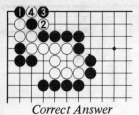

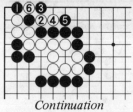

Correct Answer

Black 1 and 3 set up a ko for the life of the white group.

Continuation

After Black 3, if White plays 4, Black responds with 5 and it is still a ko.

PROBLEM 271

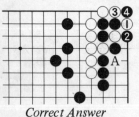

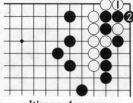

Correct Answer

White 1 and 3 set up the ko. If Black 4 to the left of 2, White plays A and it is still a ko.

Wrong Answer

If White 1, there is no ko after Black 2.

PROBLEM 272

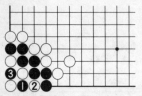

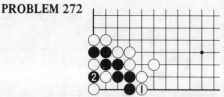

Correct Answer

Black 1 and 3 turn the corner into a double ko, so Black lives.

If White Plays First

If White plays first at 1, then Black must play 2 and it becomes a real ko.

PROBLEM 273

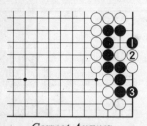

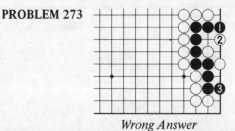

Correct Answer

Black can live by making a seki with 1 and 3. If 2 at 3, Black 3 at 2 lives.

Wrong Answer

Black 1 is answered by 2. Even if Black plays 3, he is dead.

PROBLEM 274

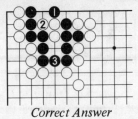

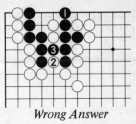

Correct Answer

Black 1 and 3 live with a seki. If White 2 at 3, Black 3 at 2 captures two stones and lives outright.

Wrong Answer

If Black 1, exchanging 2 for 3 reduces Black to a dead 4-space big eye.

PROBLEM 275

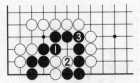

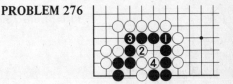

Correct Answer

Black gets a seki with 1 and 3. If 2 at 3, Black 3 at 2 and it is still a seki.

Wrong Answer

If Black 1, it becomes a dead bent-four-in-the-corner shape after 2 and 4.

PROBLEM 276

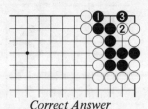

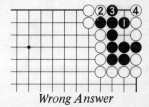

Correct Answer

Black gets a seki by playing 1 and 3.

Wrong Answer

If Black 1, Black gets a dead 5-space big eye after White 2 and 4.

PROBLEM 277

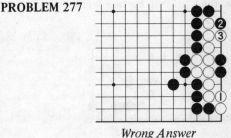

Correct Answer

White 1 and 3 are the correct order of moves for White to get seki and live.

Wrong Answer

If White 1, White is reduced to a dead 3-space big eye.

PROBLEM 278

Correct Answer

Black 1 is the vital point. If White 2, Black ataris with 3 and catches White.

Wrong Answer

Black 1 fails to capture the four stones when White answers with 2.

PROBLEM 279

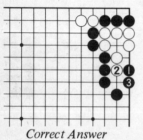

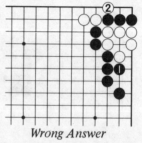

Correct Answer

Black 1 and 3 are the vital points. Black wins the capturing race.

Wrong Answer

If Black plays 1, he loses his three stones in the corner.

PROBLEM 280

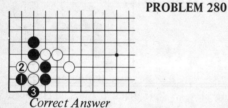

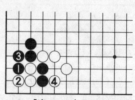

Correct Answer

Black 1 is the vital point. After 3, it is clear the Black will capture White.

Wrong Answer

If Black plays 1 and 3, he will lose three stones when White plays at 4.

PROBLEM 281

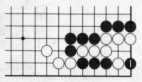

Correct Answer

Black 1 is the vital point for capturing the white stones in the corner.

Wrong Answer

If Black 1 and 3, White gets an eye up to 4, so the three black stones die.

PROBLEM 282

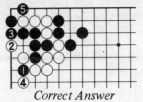
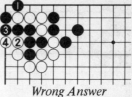

Correct Answer

If Black 1, White can't atari, so Black catches four white stones.

Wrong Answer

Playing Black 1 first lets White atari with 2 and 4. Black loses his stones.

PROBLEM 283

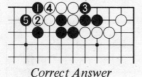

Correct Answer

Black 1 and 3 catch the white stones at the edge.

Wrong Answer

If Black 1, White will capture two black stones with 2 and 4.

PROBLEM 284

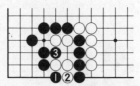
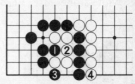

Correct Answer

Black 1 first, followed by 3, will capture five white stones.

Wrong Answer

If Black plays 1 first, he will lose his four stones on the right.

PROBLEM 285

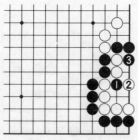
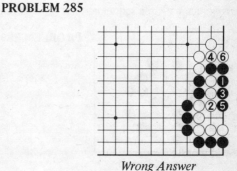

Correct Answer

If Black cuts at 1 and then plays 3, the white stones in the corner will die.

Wrong Answer

If Black lets White connect at 2, he loses his stones in the sequence to 6.

PROBLEM 286

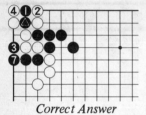

Correct Answer

Black sacrifices two stones with 1, sacrifices another by throwing in at ▲ with 5, and wins the capturing race .

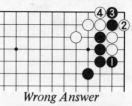

Wrong Answer

Black 3 is in the wrong direction. When White plays 6, it is clear that Black loses the capturing race.

PROBLEM 287

Correct Answer

If Black descends to 1, he will capture two white stones after Black 3.

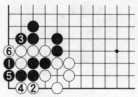

Wrong Answer

If Black 1 first, Black will lose two stones in the corner after 2 and 4.

PROBLEM 288

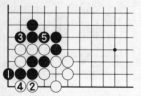

Correct Answer

After playing 1, Black will win the capturing race with the sequence to 5.

Wrong Answer

If Black plays 1, he will lose five stones in the sequence to White 6.

PROBLEM 289

Correct Answer

Black 1 forces White 2. After 3, the four white stones above will die.

Wrong Answer

Black 1 doesn't increase his liberties. Black loses four stones after White 4.

PROBLEM 290

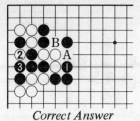

Correct Answer

Black can win the capturing race by playing 1, A, or B.

Wrong Answer

If Black plays 1, he will lose his stones on the left.

PROBLEM 291

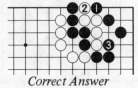

Correct Answer

Black 1 is the vital point for winning the capturing race.

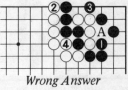

Wrong Answer

Playing 1 or A first is the wrong order. It is now Black who loses.

PROBLEM 292

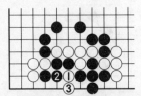

Correct Answer

After White 1 and 3, Black can't attack because he is short of liberties.

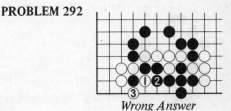

Wrong Answer

White captures a stone with 1 and 3, but he lose his five stones above.

PROBLEM 293

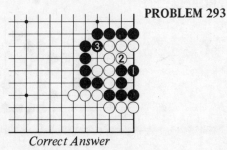

Correct Answer

If Black makes an eye with 1, he wins the capturing race.

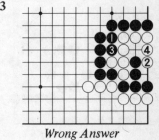

Wrong Answer

If Black plays 1, White 2 robs Black of his eye and he lives with a seki.

PROBLEM 294

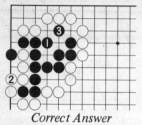

Correct Answer

Black can live by playing 1 and 3.

Wrong Answer

If Black plays 1, he ends up with a dead 3-space big eye after White 2.

PROBLEM 295

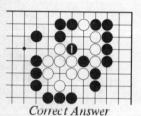

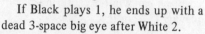

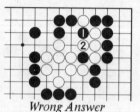

Correct Answer

Black 1 is the vital point for destroying White's eye shape.

Wrong Answer

If Black ataris with 1, White captures and gets his second eye with 2.

PROBLEM 296

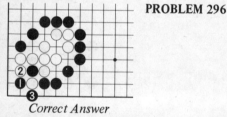

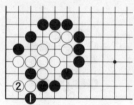

Correct Answer

Black 1 is the vital point. After Black 3, White is dead.

Wrong Answer

If Black 1, White easily gets his second eye with 2.

PROBLEM 297

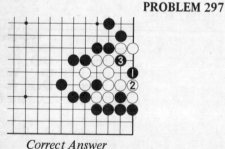

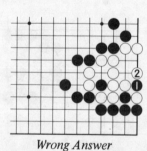

Correct Answer

If Black 1 and 3, White can't attack because he's short of liberties, so he dies.

Wrong Answer

If Black captures with 1, White easily gets two eyes with 2.

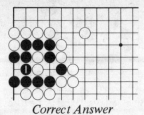

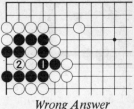

Correct Answer

Wrong Answer

After 1, if White captures a stone, Black lives by retaking three stones.

If Black connects at 1, he ends up with a dead 3-space big eye.

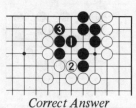

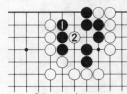

Correct Answer

Wrong Answer

Black can live by playing 1 and 3. If White 2 at 3, Black 3 at 2.

If Black plays 1, White kills Black by striking at the vital point with 2.

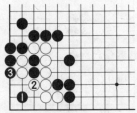

Correct Answer

Wrong Answer

Black 1 is the vital point for killing White. After 3, White has only one eye.

If Black 1, White lives with the sequence up to 4.

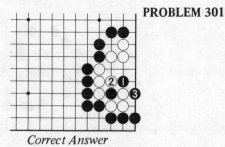

Correct Answer

Wrong Answer

Black 1 and 3 are the vital points for killing White.

Black 1 fails to kill White, as the sequence to White 4 illustrates.

PROBLEM 302

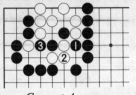

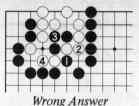

Correct Answer

Black 1 and 3 are the vital points. Even if White captures a stone, he dies.

Wrong Answer

If Black plays 1 and 3, he loses three stones after 4, so White lives.

PROBLEM 303

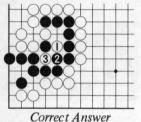

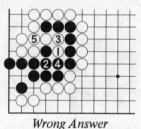

Correct Answer

Black 1, followed by 3, kills the white stones.

Wrong Answer

If Black captures with 1, he dies when White plays 2.

PROBLEM 304

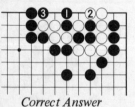

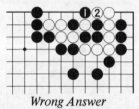

Correct Answer

Both 1 and 2 are the vital points of attack and defense. The ko starts with 3.

Wrong Answer

After White 1, Black can't avoid the ko. If he plays at 2, he dies.

PROBLEM 305

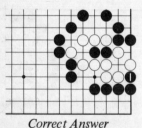

Correct Answer

Black 1 turns the white eye on the right into a false one, so White dies.

Wrong Answer

If Black plays 1 from the other side, it becomes a ko.

PROBLEM 306

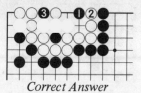

Correct Answer

After Black 1 and 3, it is not a seki: White is dead.

Wrong Answer

If Black 1, White easily lives with 2 and 4.

PROBLEM 307

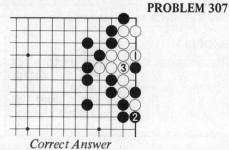

Correct Answer

White can live by making two eyes with 1 and 3.

Wrong Answer

If White 1, Black 2 prevents White from getting two eyes, so White dies.

PROBLEM 308

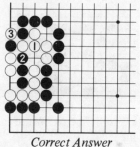

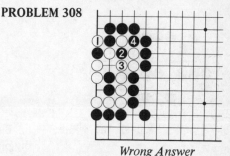

Correct Answer

White can live with a seki by playing 1 and 3.

Wrong Answer

If White first captures with 1, Black 2 and 4 kill White's group.

PROBLEM 309

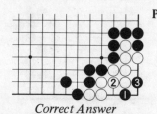

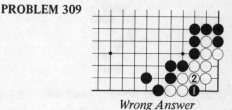

Correct Answer

Black 1 and 3 kill White by making a 'bent four in the corner'.

Wrong Answer

If Black exchanges 1 for 2, there is no way White can be killed.

PROBLEM 310

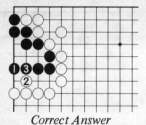

Correct Answer

Black 1 is the vital point for getting a living 4-space big eye.

Wrong Answer

If Black 1, White can create a ko with the sequence to 6.

PROBLEM 311

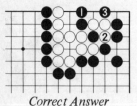

Correct Answer

Black 1 is the vital point. If White takes with 2, Black 3 kills White.

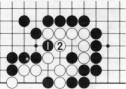

Wrong Answer

If Black connects with 1, White easily lives with 2.

PROBLEM 312

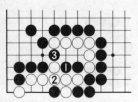

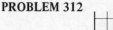

Correct Answer

Black 1 and 3 kill all the white stones.

Wrong Answer

Black 1 is ineffective. White can live by playing 2.

PROBLEM 313

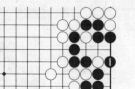

Correct Answer

Black lives by giving atari to the white stone with 1.

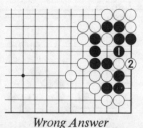

Wrong Answer

Giving atari with 1 in this direction allows White to kill him with 2.

PROBLEM 314

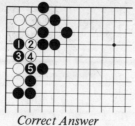

Correct Answer

The sequence up to Black 5 kills all the white stones.

Wrong Answer

Black 1 and 3 catch the two white stones, but White lives in the corner.

PROBLEM 315

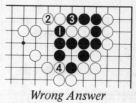

Correct Answer

Black can live with the sequence to 5. If White A, Black B.

Wrong Answer

Black 1 and 3 catch two stones, but White 4 destroys Black's second eye.

PROBLEM 316

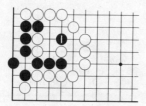

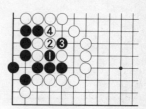

Correct Answer

Black 1 catches two white stones, so Black lives.

Wrong Answer

If Black 1 and 3, White's two stones escape, so Black dies.

PROBLEM 317

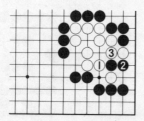

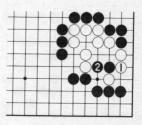

Correct Answer

White 1 is the vital point for making two eyes. White lives with 3.

Wrong Answer

If White exchanges 1 for 2, he gets only one eye, so he dies.

PROBLEM 318

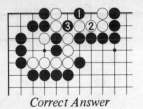

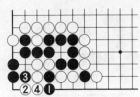

Correct Answer

Black 1 and 3 catch the four white stones on the right, so White dies.

Wrong Answer

If Black 1, White gets two eyes and lives with 2.

PROBLEM 319

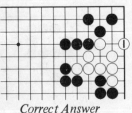

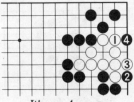

Correct Answer

White 1 is the vital point for getting two eyes and life.

Wrong Answer

If White 1, Black 2 and 4 destroy White's second eye, so White dies.

PROBLEM 320

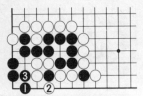

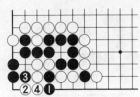

Correct Answer

Black gets his second eye in the corner with 1 and 3. If 2 at 3, Black 3 at 2.

Wrong Answer

Black 1 fails. After 2 and 4, Black can't get two eyes, so he dies.

PROBLEM 321

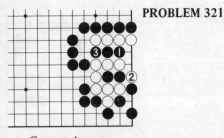

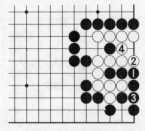

Correct Answer

Black 1 and 3 kill White. If 2 at 3, Black 3 at 2 and White still dies.

Wrong Answer

If Black 1, White can live with 2 and 4.

Correct Answer

Black 1 and 3 kill White. White can't atari Black's two stones.

Wrong Answer

Black 1 fails. White lives with 2 and 4.

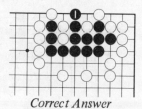

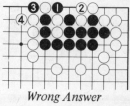

Correct Answer

Black 1 catches two stones on the left and one on the right, so Black lives.

Wrong Answer

Capturing two stones with 1 fails. Black gets only one eye after 2 and 4.

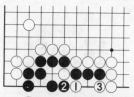

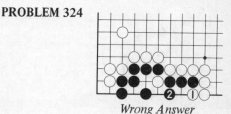

Correct Answer

White 1 and 3 are the vital points for destroying Black's eye on the right.

Wrong Answer

If White 1, Black can live by making his second eye with 2.

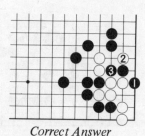

Correct Answer

Black 1 is the vital point. If White 2, Black 3 kills White.

Wrong Answer

Black 1 may look like a vital point, but White lives after 2 and 4.

PROBLEM 326

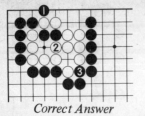

Correct Answer

Black 1 is the vital point. If White 2, Black kills White with 3.

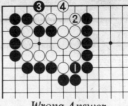

Wrong Answer

If Black plays 1 first, White lives with 2 and 4.

PROBLEM 327

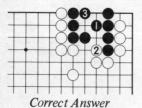

Correct Answer

Black 1 is the vital point for making two eyes. If White 2, Black lives with 3.

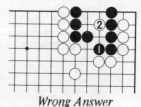

Wrong Answer

If Black 1, White 2 destroys Black's eye shape, so Black dies.

PROBLEM 328

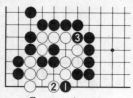

Correct Answer

Black 1 is the vital point. If White 2, Black kills White with 3.

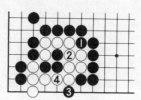

Wrong Answer

Black 1 is a bad move. After White captures with 4, he can easily live.

PROBLEM 329

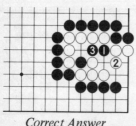

Correct Answer

Black 1 and 3 kill White. If White 2 at 3, Black 3 at 2 and White still dies.

Wrong Answer

If Black 1, White gets two eyes and lives with 2 and 4.

PROBLEM 330

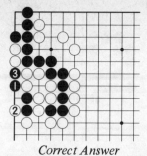

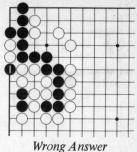

Correct Answer

Black 1 is the vital point. If White 2, Black gets another eye after 3 and lives.

Wrong Answer

If Black 1, White throws in a stone above 1 with 2, giving Black a false eye.

PROBLEM 331

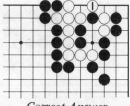

Correct Answer

White 1 captures a black stone and gives White life.

Wrong Answer

White can capture two stones with 1 and 3, but he dies after 2 and 4.

PROBLEM 332

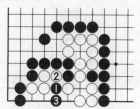

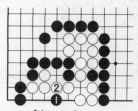

Correct Answer

After Black 1 and 3, White can't give atari to these stones, so he dies.

Wrong Answer

If Black 1, White gets his second eye at the bottom and lives with 2.

PROBLEM 333

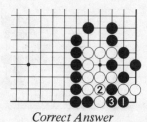

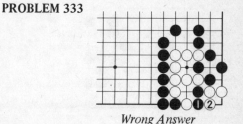

Correct Answer

Black kills White by sacrificing three stones with 1 and 3.

Wrong Answer

If Black 1, White gets two eyes with 2 and lives.

PROBLEM 334

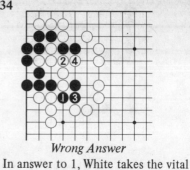

Correct Answer

Black 1 ensures the capture of three white stones. If White 2, Black 3.

Wrong Answer

In answer to 1, White takes the vital point of 2. After 4, Black's stones die.

PROBLEM 335

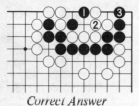

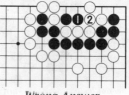

Correct Answer

Black 1 forces White 2. After 3, Black captures six stones and lives.

Wrong Answer

If Black plays 1, all his stones will die.

PROBLEM 336

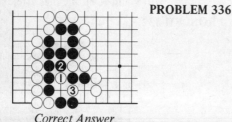

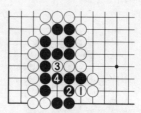

Correct Answer

White 1 and 3 kill Black by creating a false eye at the point 1.

Wrong Answer

If White 1, Black can live by making a second real eye with 2 and 4.

PROBLEM 337

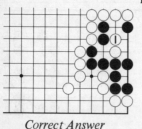

Correct Answer

White saves his two stones with 1, so Black dies.

Wrong Answer

If White 1, Black gets a second eye with 2 and 4, so he lives.

PROBLEM 338

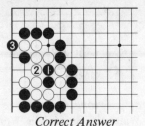

Correct Answer

Black kills White by first sacrificing two stones with 1 and then playing 3.

Wrong Answer

If Black 1 first, White lives with the sequence to 4.

PROBLEM 339

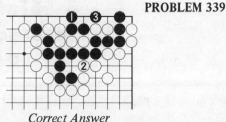

Correct Answer

Black 1 is the vital point for making life. If 2 at 3, Black 3 at 2 is essential.

Wrong Answer

Black 1 and 3 result in only one eye after White 4, so Black dies.

PROBLEM 340

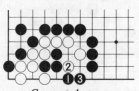

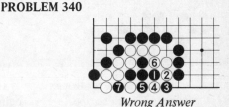

Correct Answer

Black 1 is the vital point. If White 2, Black links up with 3 and White dies.

Wrong Answer

Black 1 fails. The sequence to 7 results in a ko.

PROBLEM 341

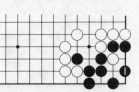

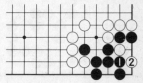

Correct Answer

Black 1 ensures that Black will get two eyes and life.

Wrong Answer

If Black 1, White 2 sets up a snapback, so Black dies.

PROBLEM 342

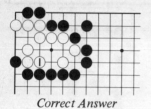

Correct Answer

White 1 is the vital point for ensuring two eyes and life.

Wrong Answer

If White 1, Black kills White by making a false eye with 2 and 4.

PROBLEM 343

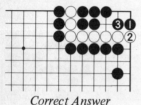

Correct Answer

Black kills White by making an eye with 1 and 3. If 2 at 3, Black 3 at 2.

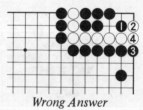

Wrong Answer

Black 1 fails. After 2 and 4, White can get either a ko or a seki.

PROBLEM 344

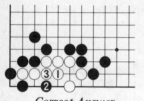

Correct Answer

White 1 is the vital point for living. After 3, the stone at 2 can't escape.

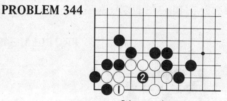

Wrong Answer

If White 1, Black strikes at the vital point of 2, killing White.

PROBLEM 345

Correct Answer

Black saves his three stones with 1 and 3, so White dies.

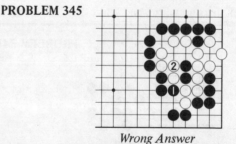

Wrong Answer

If Black 1, White catches two stones with 2 and lives.

PROBLEM 346

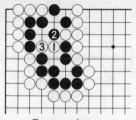

Correct Answer

If White 1 and 3, Black can't put these two stones into atari, so he dies.

Wrong Answer

If White 1, Black gets two real eyes with 2 and lives.

PROBLEM 347

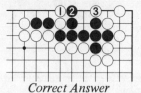

Correct Answer

White 1 and 3 prevent Black from getting two eyes, so he dies.

Wrong Answer

If the order of moves is reversed, it becomes a ko after Black 4.

PROBLEM 348

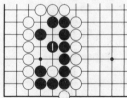

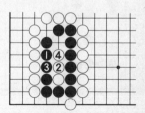

Correct Answer

Black 1 ensures that Black will get two eyes and life.

Wrong Answer

If Black 1, White sacrifices three stones with 2 and 4, and Black dies.

PROBLEM 349

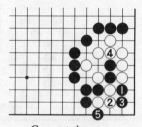

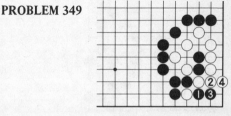

Correct Answer

Black sacrifices two stones and kills White with the sequence to 5.

Wrong Answer

If Black 1, White lives with the sequence to 4.

PROBLEM 350

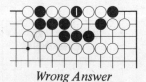

Correct Answer

Black 1 is the vital point. If White 2, Black 3 kills White.

Wrong Answer

If Black 1, White plays on the vital point of 2. After 4, White is alive.

PROBLEM 351

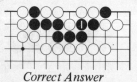

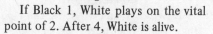

Correct Answer

If Black 1, three of White's stones at the edge will be captured, so Black lives.

Wrong Answer

Capturing with 1 fails. White retakes to the left of 1 and Black dies.

PROBLEM 352

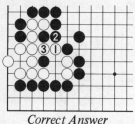

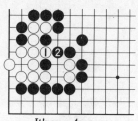

Correct Answer

White 1 and 3 catch a black stone, so White gets two eyes and lives.

Wrong Answer

White 1 will capture a black stone, but the eye he gets will be false.

PROBLEM 353

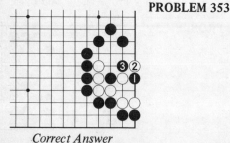

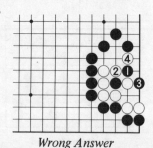

Correct Answer

Black 1 is the vital point. If White 2, Black 3 reduces White to one eye.

Wrong Answer

Reversing the order with 1 and 3 fails. After White 4, it becomes a ko.

PROBLEM 354

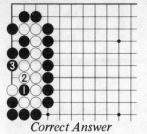

Correct Answer

If Black sacrifices a stone with 1, he can kill the white group with 3.

Wrong Answer

Black 1 fails. After White 2, it becomes a ko.

PROBLEM 355

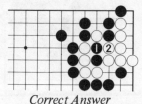

Correct Answer

Sacrificing two stones with 1 and throwing in at 1 with 3 kills White.

Wrong Answer

Black 1 and 3 fail. White will capture three stones with 4 and live.

PROBLEM 356

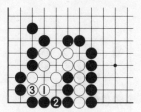

Correct Answer

White will get two eyes and life if he plays 1 and 3.

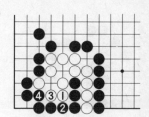

Wrong Answer

White 1 and 3 fail. After Black 4, White ends up with a false eye.

PROBLEM 357

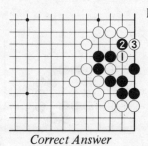

Correct Answer

White 1 and 3 are the vital points for killing Black.

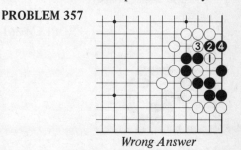

Wrong Answer

White 3 is a mistake. Black will live when he plays 4.

PROBLEM 358

Correct Answer

White 1 is the vital point. If Black 2, White lives with 3.

Wrong Answer

If White 1, Black links up to his two stones with 2, so White dies.

PROBLEM 359

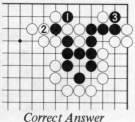

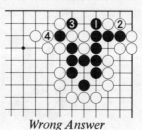

Correct Answer

Black 1 is the tesuji. If White 2, Black catches a stone with 3 and lives.

Wrong Answer

Black 1 fails. After White 2, there is no way Black can live.

PROBLEM 360

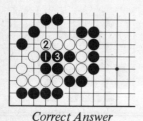

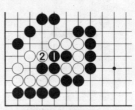

Correct Answer

Sacrificing five stones with 1 and 3 gives White a dead 5-space big eye.

Wrong Answer

If Black 1, White can get a living 4-space big eye with 2.

PROBLEM 361

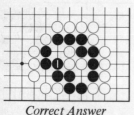

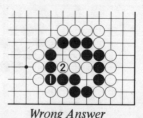

Correct Answer

Black 1 is the vital point. It is now a seki, so Black lives.

Wrong Answer

If Black 1, White 2 gives Black a dead 5-space big eye shape.

PROBLEM 362

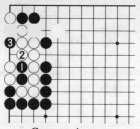

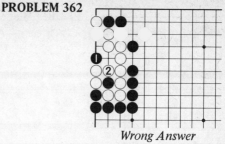

Correct Answer

Black kills White by sacrificing two stones with 1 and two more with 3.

Wrong Answer

Black 1 fails. After White 2, Black can't stop White from getting two eyes.

PROBLEM 363

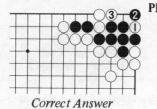

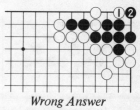

Correct Answer

The combination of 1 and 3 kills all the black stones in the corner.

Wrong Answer

If White plays 1, the result in the corner will depend on a ko.

PROBLEM 364

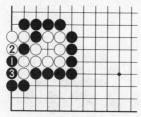

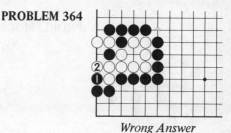

Correct Answer

Black 1 is the vital point. After 3, White is dead.

Wrong Answer

Black 1 fails. White gets two real eyes and lives with 2.

PROBLEM 365

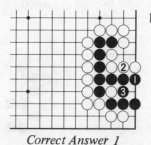

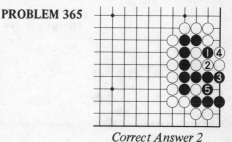

Correct Answer 1

Black 1 is the vital point. White 2 is forced. Black now gets two eyes with 3.

Correct Answer 2

Black could also play the sequence to 5. The result is the same as before.

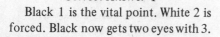

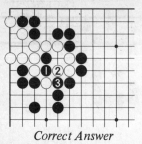

Correct Answer

Black sacrifices two stones with 1 and then gives White a false eye with 3.

Wrong Answer

If Black 1, White makes his second eye with 2 and lives.

PROBLEM 367

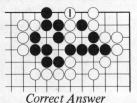

Correct Answer

If White links up his stones with 1, the black stones will die.

Wrong Answer

If White 1, Black will capture three stones and live with 2 and 4.

PROBLEM 368

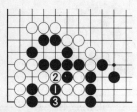

Correct Answer 1

Black can live if he captures three white stones with 1 and 3.

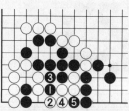

Correct Answer 2

If White answers Black 1 with 2, White loses five stones after Black 5.

PROBLEM 369

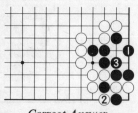

Correct Answer

Black 1 is the vital point. If White 2, Black lives with 3.

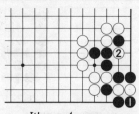

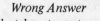

Wrong Answer

If Black takes two stones with 1, he dies after White plays 2.

PROBLEM 370

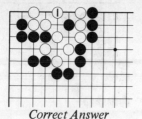

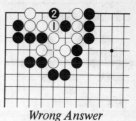

Correct Answer

White 1 is the vital point for making two eyes and life.

Wrong Answer

White 1 fails. After Black 2, White is dead.

PROBLEM 371

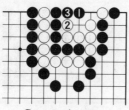

Correct Answer

Black 1 is the vital point. After Black 3, White is dead.

Wrong Answer

If Black captures with 1, White 2 catches six stones, so White lives.

PROBLEM 372

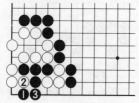

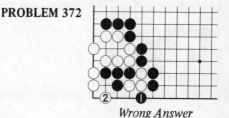

Correct Answer

Black 1 is the vital point. After 3, all the white stones are dead.

Wrong Answer

Black can capture three stones with 1, but White makes another eye with 2.

PROBLEM 373

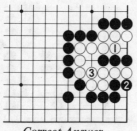

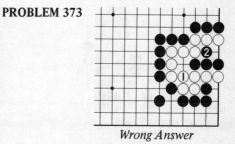

Correct Answer

White can live with a seki if he plays 1 and 3.

Wrong Answer

If White plays 1 first, he ends up with a dead 5-space big eye after 2.

PROBLEM 374

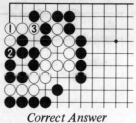

Correct Answer

Black 1 is the vital point. If Black 2, White 3 will catch eight black stones.

Wrong Answer

If White reverses the order of moves, he loses his stones after Black 4.

PROBLEM 375

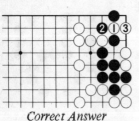

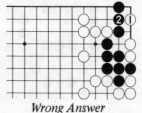

Correct Answer

White 1 is the vital point. After 3, Black can't capture White, so he dies.

Wrong Answer

If White plays 1, Black lives after playing 2.

PROBLEM 376

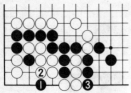

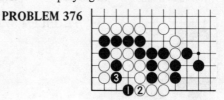

Correct Answer

Black 1 is the vital point. If White 2, Black catches four stones with 3.

Reference Diagram

If White connects at 2 in answer to 1, all of White's stones are dead after 3.

PROBLEM 377

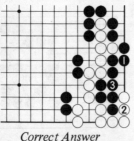

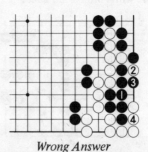

Correct Answer

If Black plays 1 and 3, his stones cannot be captured, so White dies.

Wrong Answer

If Black plays 1 first, Black will lose eight stones, so White will live.

PROBLEM 378

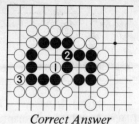

Correct Answer

Cutting at 1 to force Black 2 is the vital move. After 3, Black is dead.

Wrong Answer

White 1 fails. After Black 2, White has no follow-up move, so Black lives.

PROBLEM 379

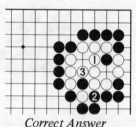

Correct Answer

White 1 is the vital point for making life. If Black 2 next, White 3.

Wrong Answer

White 1 fails. After Black 2 and 4, White is dead.

PROBLEM 380

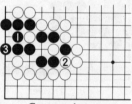

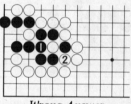

Correct Answer

Black 1 is the vital point. Black can make two eyes by playing at 3 or 2.

Wrong Answer

If Black 1, Black can't make two eyes after White 2, so he dies.

PROBLEM 381

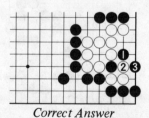

Correct Answer

Black 1 kills White. If White 2, Black links up with 3.

Wrong Answer

If Black captures two stones with 1 and 3, White lives with 2 and 4.

PROBLEM 382

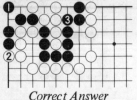

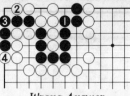

Correct Answer

Playing 1 ensures that Black will win the capturing race, so Black lives.

Wrong Answer

If Black 1, White can capture all the black stones with 2 and 4.

PROBLEM 383

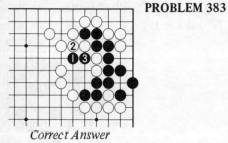

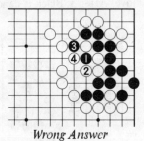

Correct Answer

Black can capture two stones and live with 1 and 3.

Wrong Answer

Against Black 1, White plays 2 and 4 and Black dies.

PROBLEM 384

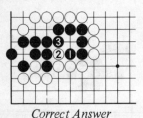

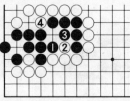

Correct Answer

Black makes two eyes and lives by playing 1 and 3.

Wrong Answer

Black 1 is a mistake. After White 2 and 4, all the black stones are dead.

PROBLEM 385

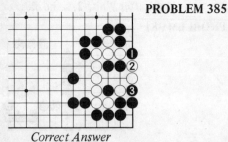

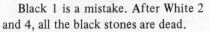

Correct Answer

Black 1 is the vital point. If White 2, Black 3 kills White.

Wrong Answer

If Black reverses the order of moves, White gets two eyes with 2 and 4.

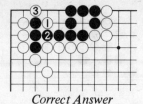

Correct Answer

After 1 and 3, Black can't capture a stone, so his group dies.

Wrong Answer

White 1 fails. Black plays 2 and gets two eyes and life.

PROBLEM 387

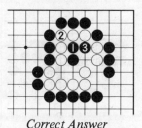

Correct Answer

If Black sacrifices three stones with 1 and 3, all the white stones die.

Wrong Answer

Black 1 fails. White lives with a seki with the sequence to 4.

PROBLEM 388

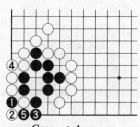

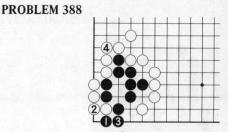

Correct Answer

If Black first sacrifices a stone with 1, he will capture two stones after 5.

Wrong Answer

If Black ataris with 1, he can't capture any stones after White 4.

PROBLEM 389

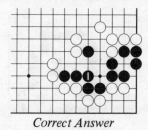

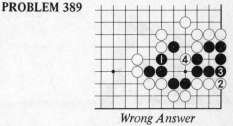

Correct Answer

Black 1 is the vital point for getting two eyes and life.

Wrong Answer

Against 1, White 2 and 4 create a shortage of liberties, so Black dies.

PROBLEM 390

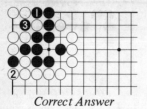

Correct Answer

Black 1 is the vital point. With 3, Black catches two stones and lives.

Wrong Answer

If Black reverses the order of moves, he can't get two eyes, so he dies.

PROBLEM 391

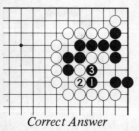

Correct Answer

Black 1 and 3 catch two stones, so Black lives.

Wrong Answer

If Black 1, the life of the black group will hinge on the result of a ko.

PROBLEM 392

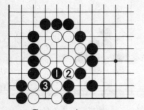

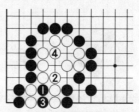

Correct Answer

Black 1 is the vital point. If White 2, Black 3 kills White.

Wrong Answer

If Black 1, White sacrifices two stones and gets two eyes with 2 and 4.

PROBLEM 393

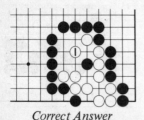

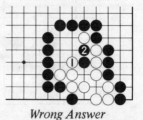

Correct Answer

White 1 catches a black stone, so White gets two eyes and life.

Wrong Answer

If White plays 1, Black escapes with 2, so White can't get two eyes. He dies.

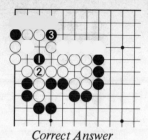
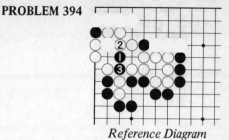

PROBLEM 394

Correct Answer

Black 1 is the vital point. If White 2, Black 3 kills all the white stones.

Reference Diagram

If White answers 1 with 2, Black 3 also kills White's group.

PROBLEM 395

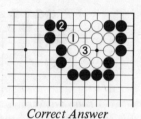

Correct Answer

White 1 is the vital point. Next, White 3 or White 3 at 2 makes two eyes.

Wrong Answer

If White 1, Black strikes at the vital point of 2 and White dies.

PROBLEM 396

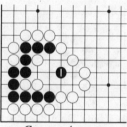
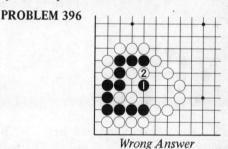

Correct Answer

Black 1 catches the three endangered white stones, so Black lives.

Wrong Answer

Black 1 fails. White can escape with 2, so Black dies.

PROBLEM 397

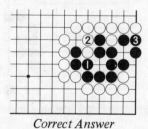
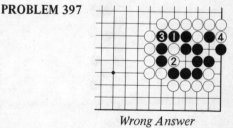

Correct Answer

Black 1 is the vital point. Next, Black 3 or Black 3 at 2 makes two eyes.

Wrong Answer

If Black plays 1 and 3, he ends up with only one eye after White 4.

PROBLEM 398

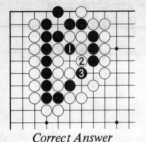

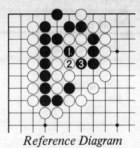

Correct Answer

Black 1 is the only move. If White 2, Black 3 will capture some stones.

Reference Diagram

If White answers 1 with 2, Black 3 will capture three stones, so Black lives.

PROBLEM 399

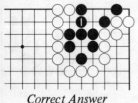

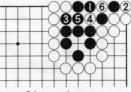

Correct Answer

Black 1 ensures that Black will get one eye at the top and live.

Wrong Answer

If Black 1, the life of the black group will hinge on the result of a ko.

PROBLEM 400

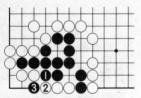

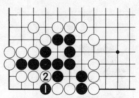

Correct Answer

Black 1 and 3 will capture at least three stones, so Black lives.

Wrong Answer

Black 1 fails. Even if Black captures two stones, he can't live.

PROBLEM 401

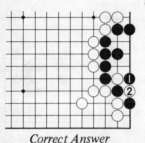

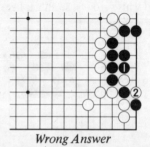

Correct Answer

The only way for Black to live is to start a ko with 1.

Wrong Answer

If Black 1, Black can't get two eyes after White 2, so he dies.

— 194 —

Correct Answer

Black kills White by making a 5-space big eye with 1 and 3.

Wrong Answer

Black 1 fails. White gets two eyes and life after he plays 2.

PROBLEM 403

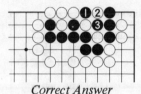

Correct Answer

Black lives by playing 1. After 2, Black catches three stones with 3.

Wrong Answer

Black 1 fails. After White 2, the black group is dead.

PROBLEM 404

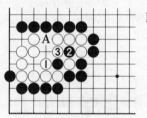

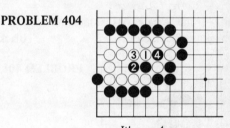

Correct Answer

White 1 is the vital point. After 3, White can get his second eye at A.

Wrong Answer

If White 1, the life of the white group will hinge on the result of a ko.

PROBLEM 405

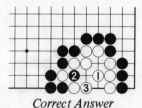

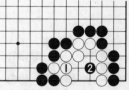

Correct Answer

White 1 is the vital point. With 3, White gets two eyes and life.

Wrong Answer

If White 1, Black strikes at the vital point of 2 and kills White.

PROBLEM 406

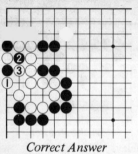

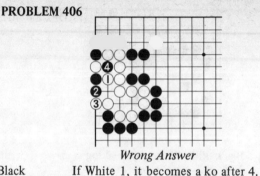

Correct Answer
White 1 is the vital point. If Black 2, White easily lives with 3.

Wrong Answer
If White 1, it becomes a ko after 4. If White 1 at 4, Black 3 kills White.

PROBLEM 407

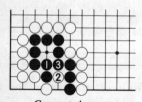

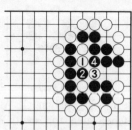

Correct Answer
White 1 and 3 catch six stones in a snapback, so Black dies.

Wrong Answer
If White reverses the order of moves, Black lives with 2 and 4.

PROBLEM 408

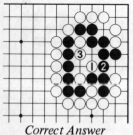

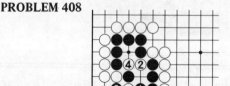

Correct Answer
Black 1 is the vital point. If White 2, Black 3 catches that stone and lives.

Wrong Answer
If Black 1, White 2 and 4 kill Black.

PROBLEM 409

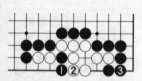

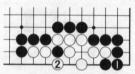

Correct Answer
After Black 1 and 3, White will get a false eye on the right, so he dies.

Wrong Answer
If Black 1, White immediately gets two eyes with 2, so he lives.

PROBLEM 410

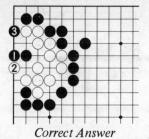

Correct Answer

Black 1 kills White since Black can now link up at 3 or one line below 2.

Wrong Answer

Black 1 fails. White catches the two black stones with the sequence to 6.

PROBLEM 411

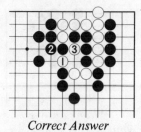

Correct Answer

White 1 and 3 catch four stones in a snapback, so White lives.

Wrong Answer

White 1 and 3 fail. After Black 4, all of White's stones die.

PROBLEM 412

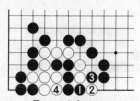

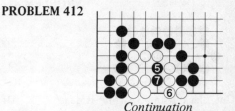

Correct Answer

Black sacrifices five stones with 1 and 3. When White plays 4 —

Continuation

Black 5 and 7 reduce White to one big eye. Black 5 at 6 also kills White.

PROBLEM 413

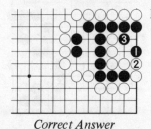

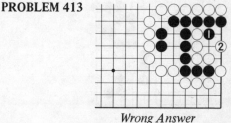

Correct Answer

Black 1 is the vital point. If White 2, Black gets another eye at 3 and lives.

Wrong Answer

If Black 1, White plays the vital point at 2 and Black dies.

PROBLEM 414

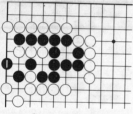

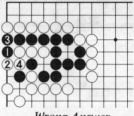

Correct Answer

If Black plays 1, the three white stones can't escape, so Black lives.

Wrong Answer

If Black 1, White saves his stones with the sequence to 4 and Black dies.

PROBLEM 415

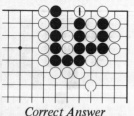

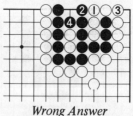

Correct Answer

White 1 kills Black. If Black takes two stones, White retakes.

Wrong Answer

If White 1, Black makes two eyes and lives with 2 and 4.

PROBLEM 416

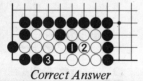

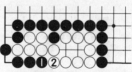

Correct Answer

After Black 1 and 3, White is dead because he is short of liberties.

Wrong Answer

If Black simply plays 1, White 2 captures three stones, so White lives.

PROBLEM 417

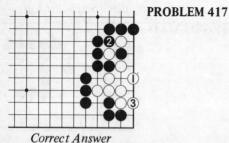

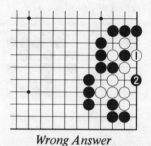

Correct Answer

White can make two eyes and live with 1 and 3.

Wrong Answer

If White takes a stones with 1, Black plays at 2 and White dies.

PROBLEM 418

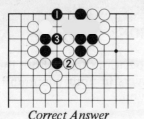

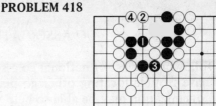

Correct Answer

Black 1 is the vital point. Next, Black 3 or Black 3 at 2 makes two eyes.

Wrong Answer

Black catches two stones with 1 and 3, but he is dead after White 4.

PROBLEM 419

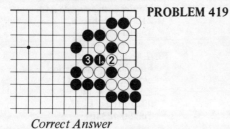

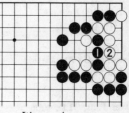

Correct Answer

Black 1 is the vital point. If White 2, Black 3 kills White.

Wrong Answer

If Black 1, Black loses three stones when White plays 2, so White lives.

PROBLEM 420

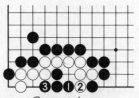

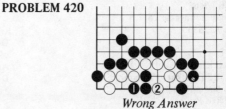

Correct Answer

Black 1 is the vital point for giving White a dead 5-space big eye.

Wrong Answer

If Black 1, White can live with a seki after he plays 2.

PROBLEM 421

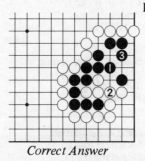

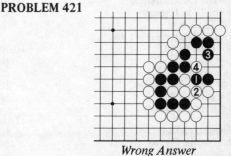

Correct Answer

Black 1 is the vital point. Next, Black 3 or Black 3 at 2 gives Black life.

Wrong Answer

If Black 1 and 3, White 4 kills Black. If 1 at 3, White 4 also kills Black.

GO ASSOCIATIONS

The following is a list of national go associations throughout the world. If you have trouble locating other go players in your community, your local go organization may be able to help you.

ARGENTINA
Argentina Go Association
c/o Mr. Guillermo E. Zucal
Aroz 2730 -6o,
1425 Capital Federal
Tel. 71-3182

AUSTRALIA
Australian Go Association,
c/o Bill Leveritt,
"Denmora",
20 Cowlishaw Street,
Bowen Hills, QLD, 4006

AUSTRIA
Osterreichischer Go-Verband,
c/o Dr. Alfred Kriegler,
1030 Wien,
Rechte Bahngasse 28/2,
Tel. 7238335

BRAZIL
Brazil Ki-in
c/o Mr. Toshikatsu Takamori,
Rua Maria Figueiredo,
350 Sao Paulo,
Tel. 289-4062

CANADA
Canadian Go Association,
c/o Mr. Tibor Bognar,
8982 St. Hubert,
Montreal, Quebec H2M 1Y6
Tel. 387-1646

CHINA
China Weiqi Association,
Ti-yu-guan Lu 9,
Peking, Tel. 753110

CZECHOSLOVAKIA
Czechoslovak Go Association,
c/o Dr. Dusan Prokop,
Laubova 8,
130-00 Praha 3, CSSR
Tel. 276565

DENMARK
Denmark Go Association,
c/o Mr. Frank Hansen,
Nordre Frihavnsgade 24,
2100 Copenhagen,
Tel. 01-269460

FINLAND
Finland Go Association,
c/o Mr. Keijo Alho,
Kuusitie 8 A 14,
00270 Helsinki 27,
Tel. 90-483401

FRANCE
Federation Francaise de Go,
B.P. 9506,
75262 Paris Cedex 06

F. R. GERMANY
Deutscher Go Bund,
c/o Mr. Martin Stiassny,
Am Burgturm 2,
D-4048 Grevenbroich I,
Tel. 02181-42021

HONG KONG
Hong Kong Go Club,
458 Nathan Road,
8th Floor, B Flat,
Kowloon,
Tel. 3-857728

HUNGARY
Hungary Go Association,
c/o Mr. Gacs Istvan,
H-1085 Budapest,
Saletrom 6

ITALY
Italian Go Association,
c/o Raffaele Rinaldi,
Via La Marmora 18,
Milano,
Tel. 02-581523

JAPAN
   Nihon Ki-in,
   7-2 Gobancho,
   Chiyoda-ku, Tokyo 102,
   Tel. 03-262-6161

KOREA
   Korea Baduk Association,
   13-4. Kwanchul-Dong,
   Chongro-gu, Seoul,
   Tel. 723-0150

MEXICO
   Mexican Go Association,
   c/o Mr. Carlos Torres,
   Watteau 15-2, Col. Nonoalco,
   Delegacion Benito Juarez 03720
   Tel. 563-2302

NETHERLANDS
   Dutch Go Association,
   c/o Mr. J. H. van Frankenhuysen,
   J. Verhulststraat 125,
   1071 NA Amsterdam
   Tel. 020-739232

NEW ZEALAND
   National Seretary, N. Z. Go Society,
   c/o Mr. Peter Rochford,
   Victoria University, Private Bag,
   Wellington
   Tel. (Home) 727267

NORWAY
   Norwegian Go Association,
   c/o Mr. Morten Skogen,
   Kzempeveien 13E,
   N-4600 Kristiansand Syd,
   Tel. 42-91373

POLAND
   Warsaw Go Club,
   c/o Mr. Leszek Dziumowicz,
   Nowy Swiat 47/3a,
   P00-042 Warszawa

RUMANIA
   c/o Mr. Gheorghe Paun,
   Institute of Mathematics Str.,
   Academiei 14,
   70109 Bucuresti
   Tel. (Home) 256754

SINGAPORE
   Singapore Go Association,
   c/o Mr. Gin Hor Chan,
   Dept. of Mathematics,
   National University of Singapore
   Kent Ridge, Singapore 0511,
   Tel. 7756666, Ext. 2083

SPAIN
   Spanish Go Association,
   c/o Mr. Ambrosio Wang An-Po,
   Vallehermoso 89,
   Madrid

SWEDEN
   The Swedish Go Association,
   c/o Mr. Per-Inge Olsson,
   Safirgangen 24,
   S-13 549 Tyreso,
   Tel. 08-770-0927

SWITZERLAND
   Swiss Go Federation,
   c/o Mr. Tamotsu Takase,
   20 Ch. des Grangettes,
   1224 Chene-bougerie, Geneve,
   Tel. 489541

TAIWAN
   Chinese Taipei Wei-ch'i Association,
   c/o Mr. C. S. Shen,
   4th Fl., Kuang Fu Building,
   No. 35 Kuang Fu S. Rd.,
   Taipei, Taiwan R. O. C.
   Tel. 7614117

UNITED KINGDOM
   British Go Association,
   c/o Mr. Norman R. Tobin,
   10 West Common Road,
   Uxbridge, Middlesex UB8 1NZ,
   Tel. 0895-30511

USA
   American Go Association
   P. O. Box 397,
   Old Chelsea Station,
   New York, N. Y. 10011

YUGOSLAVIA
   Go Savez Jugoslavije,
   c/o Mr. Peter Gaspari,
   Aleseva 3, 61210 Ljubljana —
   Sentvid. Tel. (061) 52-111